The Mule

The author's mule, Kit, just born and on her feet for the first time.

The Mule

Lorraine Travis

British Mule Society
www.britishmulesociety.org.uk

British Library Cataloguing in Publication Data
Travis, Lorraine

    The mule.
    1. Livestock: Mules & hinnies
    I.Title
    636.18

ISBN 09549061 0 1

First published in Great Britain in 1990 by
J.A. Allen & Company Limited

This edition published in 2004 by
The British Mule Society
www.britishmulesociety.org.uk

The British Mule Society are most grateful to Lorraine Travis and J.A. Allen and
Company Limited for their help and encouragement in the reprinting of this title.

Printed in Great Britain by
St Edmundsbury Press Limited, Bury St Edmunds, Suffolk

This book is dedicated to the many millions of mules which have toiled for men, often with little reward but death, and in particular to one little mule who showed me their virtues and thus led me into a fascinating world.

'In the dregs of the coffee cup the result of the labour of the sugar mule can be seen. Behind the bread we eat is the farm mule. The garments we wear are a tribute to the cotton mule; while the mine mule sends to men the coal to supply warmth and comfort and to run the engines of commerce.' (Col. J. L. Jones, US Army, 1917, quoted in *Horses and mules and national defense.*)

Acknowledgements

In addition to those people whose names appear in the text of in photograph credits, I should like to thank everyone who kindly donated photographs, and all those who have added to my knowledge of mules through their contributions to the British Mule Society's journal, *The Mule*, or through personal letters and conversations. Many of the anecdotes related here were published in the journal. I would also like to give special thanks for their help and support to Robin Borwick, Ann Chandley, Sir Cyril Clarke, Anthony Dent (without whom the history chapter would have been very short!), Betsy Hutchins, Charles MacFetridge, Bonnie Sheilds, my family, the staff of J.A. Allen (first edition) and members of the British Mule Society (this reprint).

LORRAINE TRAVIS

Definitions

Mule = male donkey × female horse
Hinny = male horse × female donkey
Donkey = ass = burro (although in the USA today burro is used to mean a feral donkey)
American Mammoth Jacks are always known as 'jackstock'

Terminology

	Horse	Donkey (UK)	Donkey (USA)	Mule/ hinny (UK)	Mule/ hinny (USA)
Male	stallion	jack (or stallion)	jack	stallion	john
Female	mare	jenny (or mare)	jennet	mare	molly

Contents

Front cover: Woody and Willow, British-born mules bred by a Catalonian jack out of a Suffolk mare, using artificial insemination techniques. (Gwyneth Wright.)

1 What is a mule?

A mule has been described as 'a cross kind of cross-bred animal', and unfortunately both for mules and for people, this view is widely held – a view which I hope this book will prove to be misguided.

Although the book is one of a series covering various breeds of horse and pony, the mule is not a breed. The word 'mule' can be used for any hybrid, from Arkwright's cotton-spinning mule to a mule canary, but we are here talking about one particular hybrid, a cross between two species of equine: the horse or pony *(Equus caballus)* and the domestic donkey *(Equus asinus)*. The word 'mule' is used for either the cross of male donkey on female horse or female donkey on male horse, although the latter cross is more correctly known as a 'hinny'.

At first glance it may seem impossible to treat under one heading an animal which can be bred from parents differing widely in size, weight, conformation and temperament. However, surprisingly, the offspring of these very different sets of parents have so much in common in appearance, mental and physical characteristics and abilities that there is no difficulty in considering them as a homogenous group.

Despite the fact that both mules and hinnies each have one horse and one donkey parent, the two crosses generally differ from each other in appearance and stature and to some extent in temperament – a fact which has been recognised since they were first bred.

The mule proper is said to have the body of a horse with the extremities of a donkey. The most noticeable points are its long ears, short thin mane, which may stand upright like a donkey's or be a little longer and flop over, and a tail which has shortish hairs on the dock a little longer than the donkey's but also has long hairs like the horse's, and is much fuller than the donkey's. The withers are low or non-existent, the back flat with a goose rump, the body flat-sided with weaker quarters than the horse, and also narrower and less deep-shouldered. The legs are, like the donkey's, straight, with small, hard, dense, upright, straight-sided hooves. The head is a little narrower than the donkey's, but otherwise very similar, except for the eyes, which are specifically mule – but difficult to describe.

Colours vary, but each country seems to have a dominant colour which in Britain is dark bay, with a lighter colour on the muzzle, around the eyes, the belly and inside the top of the legs, and darker mane and tail. There is usually – although this is not always visible – a donkey 'cross' (dorsal and wither stripe) and sometimes zebra

1

A cross between a donkey and a horse, as imagined by Bonnie Shields.

stripes on the shoulder and legs. Other colours include light bay, chestnut and black, all of these occasionally with white socks and/or a white face marking, and also, infrequently, white, roan, piebald or skewbald.

The hinny generally has the body of a donkey with the extremities of the horse. The ears are shorter than a mule's, the mane and tail longer and thicker, the legs stronger with hooves which are rounder and less upright, the body rounder and deeper, and the head shorter and narrower. The most common coat colour is blue-grey roan. However, it is noticeable that hinnies differ far more from each other than do mules, with every imaginable variation, from being almost indistinguishable from a horse, through being mule-like, to being almost indistinguishable from a donkey.

Opposite page

(*Top*) A typical mule: the author's Frances. (Photo: Derek M. Tinsley.)

(*Bottom*) A typical hinny: the author's Hatti. (Photo: Derek M. Tinsley.)

2

The voices of mules and hinnies are also different from each other, and from horses and donkeys, although both are fairly indescribable. In my experience, mules, perhaps because they are more active and outgoing, call more than hinnies, their voices being more like the donkey's than the horse's, making a sound on both exhalation and inhalation. They range from a 'bawl' – described by one person as 'the sound of an asthmatic steamboat in distress' – through a squeal, to a horse-like whicker. Hinnies only seem to call when very upset, a type of squeal which I could not attempt to describe.

Mules, having hybrid vigour, can grow taller than both parents. Weight for weight they are stronger than horses, and are much longer-lived with much longer working lives, although maturing slightly later. They rarely become ill or lame or suffer wounds, can withstand extremes of temperature, can live on frugal rations, have tremendous stamina and resilience and are exceptionally sure-footed. In his book *The Mule*, Theodore Savory quoted an experiment in which two pairs of mules and two pairs of horses of equal fitness were set to plough, and at six chosen intervals in the course of the day's work, the temperature, pulse rate and rate of breathing were recorded for each of the eight animals, as shown in the table.

	Two horse pairs	Two mule pairs
Temperature rose by	5% to 40.2 °C	5% to 38.5 °C
Pulse rate rose by	149% and 116%	55% and 59%
Respiration rose by	157% and 154%	62% and 66%

During the rest periods the mules returned more rapidly to their normal conditions.

Hinnies are said to lack hybrid vigour, and it has always been recognised that they are smaller than mules (although this may partly be due to their being carried in a smaller womb), less strong and with less stamina and hardiness.

Mules have a reputation for being obstinate and bad-tempered, but, as Theodore Savory said, 'mules, like their masters, are only stubborn and ill-tempered when badly brought up'. As with donkeys, the mule's legendary stubbornness is in fact a manifestation of its talent for self-preservation. There are times when a human finds this 'talent' annoying, when he is disobeyed by a mule, but there are many other times when it can be a great advantage: if a mule takes care of itself, then it follows that it is also taking great care of its cargo, human or otherwise. It is not for nothing that mules are chosen rather than horses to take tourists down the Grand Canyon! By intelligent handling, it is quite possible to foresee occasions on which a mule is likely to be 'stubborn' and to avoid them.

The undeserved reputation for bad temper is, I believe, due to the mule's unexpectedly sensitive and untrusting nature. Until he has learnt to trust a person, he is worried that the person may do him harm, and will take defensive action (never offensive) by kicking them, should he feel the occasion merits it. And mules are splendid kickers – they kick fast and accurately, and if a mule misses, it is because he intended to. Unfortunately many of the people who have worked with mules over the centuries have not appreciated this sensitivity, and have not understood another characteristic of the mule: that you cannot *force* him to do anything, but must persuade him, or organise his work so that he is only asked to do those things which he will want to do. Failure to appreciate this has led to many a battle between man and mule, and to the mule's bad reputation.

Mules are highly intelligent – mule devotees would say more intelligent than horses – and are very quick to learn, with a grasp of a situation which often seems little short of miraculous. This means that their handlers need to be quick-witted to stay one jump ahead of them. A well-trained and handled mule is obliging, kind, patient, persevering, calm, tolerant, sensible, loyal, affectionate, playful – and also proud, jealous and calculating. Being so intelligent, a badly trained and handled mule can be a problem.

Hinnies tend to be more donkey-like in temperament, which may be partly due to the fact that they were reared by donkeys, although this is unlikely to be the whole of the story. They are generally quieter, more compliant, less curious, less adventurous and less independent than mules. Being less sensitive and untrusting, they are less likely to kick, preferring to avoid trouble rather than confront it. Despite their reputation for being less useful than mules, there are many examples of their being much appreciated. In Ireland, for example, large numbers of hinnies were bred and used by the poorer people who could not afford horses, but found hinnies capable of more work than their donkey in agriculture, in draught, or under saddle or pack. The island of Cyprus has long been famous for the quality of its hinnies, bred by wiry pony stallions of about 13 hh out of strong donkeys the same size which produce 13 hh hinnies. The hinnies were, and still are to a lesser extent, used for riding and pack work, the mules being reserved for harness work.

The fact that there are far fewer hinnies than mules is no doubt largely due to their poor reputation, but also it is known that only a small proportion of donkey mares will conceive when served by a horse.

If difficulty is experienced in telling whether a particular hybrid is a mule or a hinny, one almost fool-proof method is to turn the animal out with a mixed group, and see what it chooses for its companions. A mule will almost invariably choose horses or other mules, while a hinny will choose donkeys or other hinnies. Two reasons suggest themselves: first, that each chooses the species which reared it, and secondly, that mules tend to be self-confident and assertive, while hinnies, like donkeys, are more self-effacing, and each joins the group with which it feels happier because they share an attitude to life.

However, so little is known about mules, compared to horses and donkeys, that this is one of many areas where we can only make guesses based on our experience.

2 The mule in history

Early times

The history of the mule is, of course, inextricably linked with the history of both horse and donkey. Without the existence of both in the same place mules could not exist. Mules are purely 'man-made' animals, the species being unwilling to interbreed in the wild except under exceptional circumstances, for example, if the male of one species is totally absent during the breeding season. This has been known amongst feral mustangs in Colorado, where mule foals have then been seen running with the mares.

The first area where both domesticated horses and wild donkeys were known to exist at the same time was the borders of Nubia around 1750 BC. It is thus likely that the first mules were bred shortly after that date. The earliest known references to mules are around 3,000 years old. The horses were rather small by our standards, probably around 12 to 13 hh, and it was discovered, probably by chance, that if a horse mare was served by one of the roaming wild jack donkeys, the foal she produced was bigger than if sired by a horse. It was fairly easy to arrange this by tethering an in-season mare outside the confines of the settlement, where a wild donkey would smell her and come along to do his duty. As the occurrence of domesticated horses and wild donkeys spread outwards rapidly from this area, so did the occurrence of mules. In Egypt, mule models were found in the pyramids, and a vase found at Thebes shows a mule-drawn chariot. Assyrian monuments also show mules, and we know they were widely used in that empire.

Mules quickly spread to the Middle East. Jews were forbidden by their religion to breed mules, because the coupling of animals of different species was held to be contrary to the laws of Nature and hence to the commandments of God (this taboo was even taken to apply to the yoking of different animals together at work). This did not, however, prevent them from buying and using the mule resulting from such forbidden union.

The Bible contains frequent references to mules, which were bred in large numbers in surrounding areas. The earliest reference may be that in Genesis 36.24: 'And these are the children of Zibeon; both Ajah and Anah: this was that Anah that found the mules in the wilderness, as he fed the asses of Zibeon his father.' There is, however, some doubt as to whether 'mules' is a correct translation. The Hittites were amongst the chief suppliers of mules, and in their script is preserved not only the first

7

Assyrian pack-mule carrying hunters' nets. A bas-relief from Nineveh.

known manual on training racehorses, but also some very early price regulations. These include a schedule of approved prices for stock: horse = 20 sheep (1 sheep = 1 shekel), ox = 20 sheep, mule = 60 sheep. Mules were expensive because they could be used in three ways: for pack transport like the donkey, for ploughing and heavy draught work like the ox, and for riding like the horse. The Hittites' only available domestic horse was seldom taller than the 13 hh wild Tarpan from which it was descended, while their mules could grow to 14 hh or more, which made them potentially very valuable, for example in wartime.

Mules were first used by the Jews in the time of King David (1010–970 BC) when they and horses supplanted donkeys as royal beasts. Many people know the story of Absolom, who was captured when he rode under an oak tree and his hair became entangled in the branches; but it is not generally remembered that he was riding a mule at the time (2 Samuel 19.9). Mules were favoured by royalty as status symbols –

King David rode a mule, and used the placing of the son chosen to succeed him, Solomon, on his personal riding mule as a symbol of his appointment as heir apparent.

The mule arrives in Europe

Greece and Rome

As the domesticated donkey spread gradually from its earliest known location, in North Africa and the Near East, into Persia, through Greece, up the Balkan Peninsular, and also by sea to Sicily, Southern Italy and such western Greek colonies as Marseilles, so the mule followed. It is not known whether 'ready-made' mules were imported in the early stages, or just the idea of breeding mule foals instead of horse foals, together with the necessary jack donkeys. The European mule was certainly identical to its eastern counterpart, although its function was different. The idea of using a mule as an officer's charger never caught on in Europe. Pack-train operatives welcomed it with enthusiasm, because a good stout mule can carry much more than a horse. Mules were also used in the Mediterranean, as in Asia, for ploughing and as a riding animal, not among royal families, but by people of high rank. The ecclesiastical upper echelons, both pagan and later Christian, took to riding mules, partly because many European cults, including at one time Christianity, had a taboo on the riding of horses by priests; this rule could be conveniently circumvented by means of a mule.

The real European innovation was the use of the mule in harness, which was comparatively rare in the ancient East. In Homerian Greece mules played a leading part in agriculture, drawing wagons, hauling timber and ploughing. There is a classic passage in Homer's *Odyssey* in which Princess Nausicaa drives a mule cart in company with her ladies in waiting, taking the palace laundry to a stream near the seashore. Mules are mentioned more than once in *The Iliad* and *The Odyssey*, confirming what we might assume from the evidence of Greek art, that they were much prized as harness animals for peaceful purposes, even though war chariots were drawn exclusively by horses.

A famous horserace, described in *The Iliad*, had as its prize a mare in foal to a jack donkey, showing mule breeding to be an occupation worthy of the upper classes; the second prize was a brood mare, third prize a large and elaborate vessel and fourth prize an attractive and accomplished female slave, which gives some idea of the

9

relative value of a mule! Harness races for mules were held at the Olympic Games for fifty years from 500 BC. Eventually the Eleans, who controlled the games, but who did not breed mules themselves because of an ancient curse placed on mules bred in Elis, discontinued the races, reportedly because the Greeks from Sicily, renowned for the quality of their mules, won so many of the races. Anaxilaus (amongst others), the tyrant of Rhegium (494–476 BC), minted coins depicting mules to celebrate his victory in a mule-cart race at the Olympic Games.

Pliny wrote of an eighty-year-old Greek mule which, no longer able to work, still followed the others as though he wanted to help, a devotion to duty which so pleased the Athenians that they gave him the keys to the grain market. Greek vases commonly depict mules in various activities, including mule carts filled with wedding parties, and Dionysus, god of fertility, riding a mule. This, to us, seems to have been an Ancient Greek joke, in view of the fact that mules are generally infertile.

The importance of mule breeding in the Roman world is clear from Varro, writing in the second half of the first century, and Columella, who lived and wrote about a century later. Pliny the Elder (AD 23–79) wrote at length about their breeding, characteristics, attributes and stubborn temper in his *Natural History*, although some of his facts and some of his advice on mule breeding are questionable. Later, Claudian praised the draught mules of Roman Gaul for their intelligence and obedience. The Romans' veterinary manual, was, incidentally, called *Mula Medicina*.

The many depictions of the mule on sculptured reliefs, mosaics and the like, combined with additional literary evidence from the Theodosian Code and similar sources, indicate that the mule was widely used in the Roman world for pulling carts and other vehicles (for which it was preferred to horses) and for pack work. It seems that in the northwest provinces at least (including, almost certainly, Britain) and presumably throughout the empire, the mule, together with the ox for pulling heavy loads, was one of the main sources of tractive power. The ceremonial *carpentum* (a two-wheeled covered carriage) drawn by mules was used by aristocratic ladies, including queens and later priestesses. Various other types of two- or four-wheeled carts were used, and up to ten mules at a time. The use of mule teams, and the ill-treatment they received which led them to be replaced at frequent intervals, created a need for large numbers of mules. The Romans, incidentally, had extremely large and well-organised public transport and postal systems, and mules were used for these almost exclusively.

Even larger numbers of mules were used by the army, and many were used for other tasks such as pulling barges, as members of long teams dragging large blocks of marble for building work, pushing the curious type of grain-harvesting machine invented by the Romans, or even, in their old age, turning the baker's mill.

Britain

The earliest known British mule is that believed to have been traced in Roman remains at Billingsgate Buildings on the northern side of Lower Thames Street, London, in 1974. A jawbone was found amongst domestic rubbish which, according to the archaeozoologist P. L. Armitage, is almost certainly that of a mule – and one which has been rather severely treated. A tombstone at Chesters, Hadrian's Wall, of a Roman trooper of the third century, shows him mounted on a mule. It seems likely that the mules would have been brought to Britain by the Romans rather than bred there. Once the Romans had left, in AD 410, the mule seems to have more or less disappeared from Britain for several centuries, although it was probably still bred in small numbers. Anthony Dent in *Donkey* suggests that evidence of this may be found in place names such as Moulsoe in Berkshire, Moulscombe in Sussex, the Moultons in Cheshire, Lincolnshire and Norfolk, Mulgrave in North Yorkshire, Muncaster (once Mulecaster) also in North Yorkshire and another in Cumbria, all of which date from the early days of Saxon settlement and mean 'mule farm' or something similar, or else denote the estate of a man named or nicknamed Mule – because he was like a mule?

As well as spreading into Europe, mules naturally spread into other areas, across North Africa, into Ethiopia where many mules are bred, but never very far south because the climate was not suitable for horses; and also into Asia, particularly China, where many were used. Unfortunately little information has come to light about mules in these countries and the dates of their arrival, although we can assume that timing and uses were similar to the European mule. A few isolated recordings have been passed down, such as the fact that the prophet Mohammed (AD 567–632) rode a mule in battle, and that in 1274 Marco Polo praised the Turkoman mules he encountered in Central Asia.

From early Norman times, the evidence of the existence of mules in Britain is much more conclusive, for example in 1116 the Abbey of Burton-on-Trent kept thirty-six brood mares and three Spanish jack donkeys – a good sized mule-breeding establishment. However, here again references to mules are few and far between. A mule is shown on the Bayeux Tapestry, and we know that the breeding of superb

Lord Burleigh riding a mule or hinny in the late sixteenth century. (Bodleian Library, Oxford, Poole. 38.)

donkeys and mules in the French region of Poitou was well developed and widely appreciated from the tenth century onwards.

Around the fifteenth century mules began to increase in popularity in Europe, including Britain, although in northern Europe at least they were still mainly used by the ecclesiastics. The Monk of the fifteenth-century Lydgate's continuation of *The Canterbury Tales* is shown by the illuminator riding on a mule, whereas Chaucer had given him a palfrey. Cardinal Wolsey (1473–1530) had a pair of very fine mules on which he toured the country. This was the end of a long tradition which did not outlive the Reformation by very much, but the last traces of which were to be seen in the early seventeenth century, kept up by laymen in certain offices. Lord Burleigh (1520–1598), father of the first Robert Cecil, rode a mule (or more probably a hinny), and right down to the reign of James I (1603–1625) the Lord Chancellor and certain senior law officers of the Crown always rode a mule on official occasions. No doubt this is something that 'rubbed off' on lawyers and civil servants from the days when approximately half the lawyers were churchmen, practitioners of canon, not civil and criminal law. (In England the ecclesiastical lawyer was distinguished from other churchmen by the fact that the former always rode a docked mule.)

Although the mule then more or less went out of fashion, there were always a few enthusiasts who kept the tradition of mule breeding alive. Several of the landed gentry in Britain, who had no doubt come across mules on their travels in southern Europe, set up their own mule-breeding studs. One such was the Duke of Bridgewater, and when James Brindley's first canal was built in the 1760s on the Duke's instructions, the first boat on it was pulled along by two of the Duke's mules. In fact, mules continued to be used on British canals (as well as those in other countries, notably the USA and on the Panama Canal) until well into the 1950s.

Other European mules

In the Mediterranean region, mules had remained in favour continuously. The largest known pack train of 15,000 Spanish mules was called into the service of the Crown of Castile and Léon by Queen Isabella. The clergy continued to ride mules (the Pope was never seen mounted on anything else, as witnessed in Alphonse Daudet's delightful story, 'La Mule du Pape', in which the mule waited seven years to get its own back on a young man who had played a trick on him), and the wealthier laymen also rode mules as a substitute for palfreys, as did several Mediterranean kings. This tradition continued in the Mediterranean area long after it had virtually

Hunting on a mule. Engraving by J. Stradanus, sixteenth century. (Reproduced by courtesy of the Trustees of the British Museum.)

disappeared from northern Europe, and indeed certain types of horse whose work could be done equally well or better by mules became either very scarce or even absent altogether. These categories ranged from horses for ploughing and heavy draught work to elegant town hacks, and even when coaches were introduced in the seventeenth century, carriage horses were not bred – mules were used.

The one exception to the rule that mules were rare in northern Europe was the famous mule-breeding area of Poitou. For around a thousand years this area has been considered the producer of Europe's finest mules. As early as the twelfth century a Roman prelate demanded from the Duke of Aquitaine a large and beautiful mule from his province. Both the jack donkeys and the mares used in Poitou were and are bred especially for mule production, and are large, strong, and heavy-boned. The mules are very big, heavy, strong and good-looking, and excellent workers – around 50,000 were bred each year in the second half of the nineteenth century, prices reaching £400.

Poitou mules had their heyday in the late nineteenth century, when the Poitou jack donkey was the most important quadruped in Poitou. Their owners were allowed to call themselves *maître* and were held in high regard by their fellows. In about 1870 there were 160 stud farms with 465 jack donkeys. The mares of cart-horse type favoured for mule breeding were owned by a different set of people, and horse breeding and donkey breeding tended to be found in distinct areas of Poitou. (More details of Poitou mules can be found in Chapter 5.)

Mules in the New World

When the Spanish explored and conquered large parts of Central and Southern America in the early sixteenth century they took their mules with them. Around 1530, ten years after Cortés' conquest of Mexico, the first shipment of jack donkeys was sent out to breed mules from the horses (or their offspring) that the Spanish had already taken with them. In these areas high-quality mules, particularly pacing mules, are still bred and are highly prized – and highly priced! This is notably so in Peru, where their value as pack animals immediately became obvious, partly because the most fertile part of the country is separated from the coast by a sandy desert region where llamas, Peru's indigenous form of transport, cannot operate. In any case, the llama can at best only carry half a mule-load. But also in Peru there has always been a keen demand for mules as riding animals. This is true in many parts of other South American countries as well.

Some mules were smuggled across the border from Spanish to British territory in the south and west of what is now the USA. So far as can be ascertained the first mules in the 'American West' came from New Mexico up the Santa Fe Trail, although the existence of jack donkeys in some of the thirteen Colonies advertised for mule production antedates the revolutionary war (1775–1783).

By the eighteenth century mule breeding was a flourishing industry in Spain, Italy and France, but until late in that century mules were virtually unheard of in North America with the exception of the few Spanish mules in the south and west and a few poor New Forest-bred mules imported by the British. George Washington did much, however, to encourage their use. He saw the need for improved transport to aid the development of America's great potential, and believed that mules, with their strength, longevity, economy and resistance to disease, were the answer. Even before his inauguration in 1789 the first president wrote to King Charles IV of Spain requesting permission to buy some Spanish donkeys of the best quality. Since at that time Spanish exports and imports were rigidly controlled, the king avoided establishing a commercial precedent by making a gift of two Andalusian donkeys of each sex. Only one of the jacks, Royal Gift, and the two jennies survived the journey, and arrived at Mount Vernon in 1785. In February 1789 the following advertisement was placed in the Philadelphia newspaper.

ROYAL GIFT

A JACKASS of the first race in the Kingdom of Spain will cover mares and jennies at Mount Vernon the ensueing spring. The first for ten and the latter for fifteen pounds the season. Royal Gift is four years old, is between 14½ and 15 hands high, and will grow, it is said, until he is 20 or 25 years old. He is very bony and stout-made, of a dark colour with light belly and legs. The advantages, which are many, to be derived from the propogation of asses from this animal (the first of the kind that ever was in North America) and the usefulness of mules bred from a jack of his size, either for the road or team, are well known to those who are acquainted with this mongrel race. For the information of those who are not, it may be enough to add that their great strength, longevity, hardiness and cheap support, give them a preference of horses that is scarcely to be imagined. As the Jack is young, and the General has many mares of his own to put to him, a limited number only will be received from others, and these entered in the order they are offered. Letters directed to the subscriber, by Post or otherwise, under cover to the General, will be entered on the day they are received, till the number is completed, of which the writers shall be informed to prevent trouble or expense to them.

John Fairfax,
Overseer

Feb. 23, 1786

The language of the advertisement indicates clearly that mules were already well known in the Colonies; hence it is evident that mule production was well established there long before the time this advertisement appeared. Although George Washington was not the first to breed mules, his approval and action stimulated mule production and use because of the esteem in which he was held.

In 1786 Washington's old comrade-in-arms the Marquis de Lafayette sent him a Maltese jack, Knight of Malta, and two Maltese jennies; smaller at 14 to 14.2 hh, but less leggy and of better conformation for mule breeding, and their offspring, in a better environment, grew larger than them. Knight of Malta was crossed with one of the Andalusian jennies to produce the jack which George Washington named Compound, and Compound was put to mares on Washington's Mount Vernon estate to produce excellent mules – far superior to the best horses for work – some of which sold after his death for nearly $200.

Henry Clay of Lexington, Kentucky, a Virginian politician, also imported several jacks into Kentucky, which became one of America's greatest donkey- and mule-breeding areas because of the ideal climate, and the great demand for mules for use in agriculture. Some experts believe that to him belongs the honour of having made the first important and valuable importation of jackstock. From 1827 onwards he imported several donkeys, mainly from Malta, but a few finer-boned animals from Spain. In about 1840 Young Everett of Montgomery County, Kentucky, bought a Spanish jack at Charleston, South Carolina, which, because of his great size, was named Mammoth. When he was crossed with the finer stock of Henry Clay, the offspring were of excellent quality, and laid the basis of Kentucky's reputation as a centre for fine mule-breeding jack donkeys. Almost all of the great jacks to the present day can be traced back to Mammoth.

According to the jackstock expert Frank Mills, the foundation stock of the American Mammoth Jack, which is what the very big jack donkeys came to be called, included Andalusian, Catalonian, Maltese, Majorcan and a few Poitou donkeys, to give more bone and strength.

George Washington's jacks travelled far afield from their Mount Vernon home, spreading rapidly from Virginia throughout the southern states. In the northern states this trend was less marked, both for climatic reasons and because it was said that the negro drivers and grooms, of which there were few in the north, worked better with the mules than white men. The climatic distribution of donkeys and mules, as in the Old World, was generally south of the 40° N line, as north of this provision would have to be made for wintering the donkeys. The southern states, particularly Kentucky, but including Tennessee, Mississippi, Oklahoma, Texas, Kansas, Illinois, Nebraska and Arkansas, became and still are the main areas for mule breeding.

The opening up of the American West from the 1840s onwards was almost entirely due to the mule, although horses and oxen also played their part, the former mainly as riding animals, the latter for pulling heavy loads at slow speeds. Mules were the principal motive power for the wagons, and on arrival the pioneers used them for agricultural draught work, rounding up stock, and harness work, and thousands were used under pack by traders supplying the new settlers. The longest continuous stage run, the Butterfield Southern Overland Mail Stage Line, established in 1853, was 2,759 miles from St Louis to San Francisco. The run took twenty-three days, of which nearly half were in the deadly hot and dry desert, and mules did the desert stretch because they could stand the heat and dryness better than horses.

Mules also played a large part in the building of roads and railways, which speeded up the opening of the West, both carrying materials and operating the drag-lines, scrapers and so on for levelling gradients. They then also pulled the canal boats, although the railways they helped to build did them out of a job.

Probably the most important use of mules, however, was in agriculture, particularly in the southern states, and this proved a tremendous incentive to breeding more and better mules. The plantation economy which developed in the Deep South with its emphasis on cotton and maize and tobacco would have been unworkable in pre-mechanisation days without an abundant supply of mules. Mules thrive on maize, and the large amount of this available meant that they could work all day with only a small amount of straw as bulk fodder, unlike horses, which can only be fed maize in moderation.

Most of the mules in the northern states were imported from the south, as this was more economic than breeding them in the colder climate.

After the United States Emancipation Proclamation of 1865, freed slaves were given a plot of land, seeds and a mule with which to keep themselves, so the mule became the symbol of 'Black Freedom' of which vestiges still survive today. When the petition was presented for the establishment of Martin Luther King Day, in memory of the civil rights leader, it was carried to the Capitol on a mule-drawn wagon, and in the great Peace Marches to Washington, mules and carts have always held a conspicuous place.

One of the most famous uses of mules in American history, although it only lasted for five years from 1883 to 1888, was to haul borax from the mines in Death Valley in

19

A twenty-mule team in Death Valley used by US Borax during the 1880s. (US Borax and Chemical Corporation.)

California to the nearest railhead. Teams of twenty mules (or usually eighteen mules and two heavy horses as wheelers, closest to the wagon) pulled approximately 28 tons, consisting of two wagons, their load of borax, two men and a loaded water tanker, on a 165-mile journey which took ten days, turning round immediately for the return journey.

The road was virtually non-existent, with steep inclines, massive boulders and shifting sands, and the climate ranged from well below zero at night to 150 °F in summer. There was no natural water supply or fodder, and no human habitation, so supplies for the whole journey had to be taken along, some of them dropped off at each way-station on the outward journey, to be picked up and consumed on the journey home. The team was driven by one man (the other leading when necessary, and operating the brakes on the rear wagon) using a jerk line attached to the bit of the near leader – a steady pull for a left turn, several jerks for a right turn, a shout and the brakes slammed on hard to stop. The mules had to be not only very tough, but also very intelligent. The great length of the 'turnout' made taking corners in the conventional manner impossible, so a number of the mules nearest the wagon had to learn to jump over the chain which ran from the front to the back of the team and pull outwards to prevent the team running into the rock on the inside of the bend. At first they had to be ordered to jump, but they soon learned to do it when they saw the jerk-line mule begin to make the turn. It was a very hard and dangerous life for mules and men, which is why it became so famous.

Until 1888 the only records of jackstock breeding were kept by the breeders themselves, and information is hard to come by. In 1888, however, the first registry association of American Jackstock was started, the time being more than ripe for such an organisation: the American Breeders Association of Jacks and Jennets. The aim was to adopt 'such standard for the admission of jacks and jennets to the stud book as will insure the improvement of the stock and command the respect of intelligent and progressive breeders'. In 1912 it was decided to organise the incorporation of a company for the registration of jacks and jennets, and the Standard Jack and Jennet Registry of America was set up. By this time, the standard of breeding, hitherto very mixed because no one had bothered much, had been raised enormously. To be eligible for registration, donkeys had to be the progeny of registered stock or to be of a minimum height – variable over the years: jacks 14.2 to 15.2 hh, jennies two inches less, which standard was lowered in 1942 to 14 and 13.2 hh, not through a desire for smaller jacks, but a sign of the times; the demand for mules was decreasing, and fewer big jacks were being bred.

A team of mules ploughing in the USA today, just as they did in the past. (Photo: Bonnie Shields.)

The high regard in which mules were held is reflected in the relative average values of mules and horses:

1 January 1880	Mules $61.26	Horses $54.75
1890	78.25	68.64
1900	53.56	44.61
1906	98.31	80.72

In 1850 the mule population of the United States was 559,000 and in the following ten years the number increased by 100 per cent. In 1900 there were 3,321,131 mules in the USA, in 1910 4,424,384 and in 1920 5,432,000, by far the highest number of mules in any country.

Vast numbers of mules were exported from the USA:

1880	Mules 5,198	Value $532,362
1885	1,028	127,580
1890	3,544	447,108
1895	2,515	186,452
1900	43,369	3,919,478
1901	34,405	3,210,267
1902	27,586	2,692,298
1903	4,294	521,725
1904	3,658	412,971
1905	5,826	645,464

The large increase between 1895 and 1900 was due to the South African wars.

The mule population in the twentieth century declined gradually, from 5,432,000 in 1920 to 5,131,000 in 1931, 2,544,000 in 1948 and a mere 1,603,000 in 1954, the number still falling rapidly at that date.

Mules in twentieth-century Britain

In Britain in recent times the number of mules used has been comparatively small, and the amount of information available even smaller! They were either bred by a few enthusiasts or – probably the majority – were ex-army animals, particularly in the first half of the twentieth century. Agriculture was probably the main use, followed by various forms of light and heavy draught work including coal haulage and pulling canal barges. They were used on the Midlands canals right up until the 1950s, the last users being Joe and Rose Skinner, whose mule Dolly pulled their boat *Gifford*, carrying gas for Mr Bunford of Shebdon on the Oxford and Coventry Canals. She only retired, in fact, in 1971.

Mules, have, however, not been highly prized by the majority of Britons, with the notable exception of ex-soldiers who had experience of them overseas; in fact, they have frequently been the objects of derision. The lack of suitable donkeys for breeding big, good quality mules meant that, once the army's supply dried up, and with mechanisation increasing, mules were reduced drastically in number.

Mules at work in London around the turn of the century. (Reproduced from Prof. C. Bryner Jones, *Livestock of the farm*, Gresham, 1916, by permission of the Syndics of Cambridge University Library.)

Joe and Rose Skinner's Dolly, who worked on the Oxford and Coventry Canals until 1971, drawn by Donald J. M. Smith.

Mules in other countries

In Africa, south of the equator, there were no wild horses or donkeys, their ecological place being taken by the zebra, so there were no mules in ancient times. A slow spread south of donkeys from the Sudan into Ethiopia took place, and the high altitudes and dry climate suited the donkey to perfection. Transport has never been totally mechanised here, because of the mountainous terrain, and mules (particularly for high-ranking people, including the Emperor Haile Selassie) have been preferred to the horse. Mules were first bred in South Africa in Napoleonic times for military purposes, an industry which continued into this century, fluctuating as military demand fluctuated, but with mules also being used for agriculture until very recently, and still in small numbers in the less highly developed countries.

In Asia mules continued to be used in large numbers in many countries, particularly as the native horses were little more than ponies, although very strong and hardy. In China, which is today a large user of mules, they were always extremely common for all types of work: agriculture, light draught (when they were often harnessed with ponies), pack work and riding. From the Himalayas to the Gobi desert to the jungles of Southeast Asia, mules found their place.

In Australia donkeys arrived fairly late, the first being imported to New South Wales from India, Spain and Mexico from 1792 onwards, and were at their height in the early 1900s when the northwestern territories were being developed. Many sheep stations also bred mules, quality jacks being imported from Spain. Mechanisation, around the time of World War II, led to a virtual end to mule breeding in Australia.

3 Military use of the mule

The value of mules for military purposes has been appreciated virtually as long as they have been bred. They were used for much the same purposes and using the same equipment as civilian animals. In fact it is only in fairly recent times that armies, as a matter of course, owned any animals – they generally commandeered civilian animals, and usually their owners to work with them, as and when required, which was far cheaper than keeping their own animals unemployed during peace time. It did, however, have many disadvantages in terms of insufficient numbers, poor quality animals which were not used to hard work, poor equipment, the men's lack of military discipline and loyalty, the time it took to buy and train the mules, and the disruption to civilian commercial traffic.

Ancient cultures

The earliest military use of mules was for pack work, carrying the vast quantities of supplies and armaments needed by an army on the move. The table shows the loads and speeds of which various animals are capable, and demonstrates part of the advantage mules have over other animals under pack. These figures are for average-

Animal	Load (kg)	Km per 7 hr day
Horse	60	39.2
Mule	90	91.0
	136	58.0
	181	46.2
Donkey	54	39.2
Buffalo	250	21.0
Oxen	55	24.0
Yak	75–160	19.6
Camel	120–175	28.0
Llama	40	31.5
Elephant	460	24.5

(Prepared by Eve Iverson, formerly Animal Transportation Officer with the US Army, reproduced from 'Animal-Based Transportation', *Global Mobility*, September 1988.)

A Roman *carro-ballista* depicted on Trajan's column in Rome.

sized animals, and are not maximum loads, but those which are most suitable for long distances for continuous periods.

They were also extremely valuable, because of their extra height, as mounts for anyone who had to see or to be seen above the heads of the rank and file mounted on horses, such as officers, standard bearers, drummers and trumpeters. The Hittites are probably the best-known early users of mules for military purposes, whose value in this respect was probably the main impetus for those who had not previously bred mules to do so.

The Persian Army of Xerxes in 480 BC attacked the Greeks at the Pass of Thermopylae, having mules in its train, one of the earliest references to the use of mules in the supply lines of armies. Alexander the Great (356–323 BC) was said to

Sixteenth-century artillery mule carrying ammunition to the siege of Montereggio in the Italian wars of Charles V and Francis I. Engraving by J. Stradanus. (Reproduced by courtesy of the Trustees of the British Museum.)

have a chariot drawn by twelve mules, of which he was very proud, although like others of his period he chose a horse, the famous Bucephalus, for riding. His generals, however, rode mules into battle because of their extra height. Alexander's funeral bier was drawn by sixty-four mules, four yoke poles hitching each of four teams of four and the mules wearing gold wreaths and little gold bells on their cheeks.

As with use by civilians, the use of mules as draught animals really began in earnest as they spread into Europe. The Roman and Greek armies used them for pack work and for riding, particularly for triumphal and ceremonial entries into cities, but also to pull vehicles containing supplies, and – an innovation – to draw sharp-shooting arrow firing machines (*carro-ballistae*) mounted on two-wheeled carts – a sort of early mobile field gun (see p. 29).

More recent times

There are reports of many mules being used in all the major campaigns in recent times – the Napoleonic and Peninsular Wars, Afghanistan, the Crimea, the American Civil War, Abyssinia, South Africa, the Russo-Japanese War, and of course by the British in India who were fighting, using mules as the main form of transport, almost continuously from 1836 until Indian Independence in 1947.

Until the nineteenth century there is little record of the British Army using mules in large numbers, but in 1802 the Royal Waggon Train was established to provide general transportation, while the Artillery Train was manned by artillery drivers. Due to economies, the Royal Waggon Train was disbanded in 1833. The Duke of Wellington had 53,000 British troops supported by 10,000 pack mules during the Peninsular War, the Duke preferring pack to wheeled transport, because the latter was much slower and less flexible.

By the time of the Crimean War, the transport situation in the British Army was disastrous: only seventy-five mules and a few carts were available to be landed in the Crimea to maintain 33,000 men! The public outcry led to the establishment of the Land Transport Corps with 30,000 horses in the Crimea, and in 1856 this was replaced by the Military Train (which in turn was replaced by the Army Service Corps in 1869) which once more consisted of horses. It had begun to be recognised that mules were at their best under pack.

Thanks to Florence Nightingale, the Crimea was the scene of great advances in military medicine, but evacuation of casualties to the hospitals was still a great problem (and very painful). The British Army tried a number of 'ambulances': four-

Mule-borne cacolets in
the Crimean War.

wheeled wagons (useless on poor ground, so they often could not get near the front),
lighter two-wheeled carts (still limited and uncomfortable), and eventually mule-
borne litters and chairs, the first providing stretcher transport, mounted on the pack
saddle high above the mule's back and running fore and aft, the second providing
sitting accommodation in 'cacolets' – two comfortable armchairs mounted either side
of the saddle, with the occupants facing forwards. These 'ambulances' could go
anywhere, move quickly, and were very (or relatively) comfortable. They were
copied by other armies, and are still in use today.

   In the Abyssinian expedition of 1867 British and Indian Army troops on a
combined basis made extensive use of pack mules over difficult country.

US Army

In the meantime, the US Army had become very well organised, in the Civil War and
Indian Wars. The army travelled far from supply depots, in inhospitable country,
and needed to have regular supplies provided by mule trains. These followed up the

fighting echelon across country impassable to wheeled traffic, as close as was tactically possible. Indeed, great tactical skill was needed by the Train Master to keep near enough to the cavalrymen to replenish their cartridge pouches and their stomachs as often as necessary without exposing his mules to the highly mobile enemy. Each train consisted of one pack master, one cargador or assistant pack master, one cook, one blacksmith, ten packers (total fourteen men), one bell mare, fourteen saddle mules and fifty pack mules. (The bell mare was commonly used to lead a string of mules who would follow her through thick and thin, and come back to her in the morning if they had been turned out to graze at night.) Eight of these trains served in the United States. The mules were 13.2 to 16 hh, about 850 lb in weight and carried 350 lb.

Wagons were pulled by two, four or six mules. Two mules pulled a wagon of 1,550 lb plus a 1,000–2,000 lb load; four mules pulled loads of 2,000–2,400 plus the wagon.

These supply lines had been developed between 1830 and 1860, a period that witnessed the gradual ascendence of the pack mule. In the earlier days the wagons were more common, and had the advantage of being easily and quickly loaded, and could be used for carrying the sick and wounded. Later, however, pack mules more

US Army supply wagon, nineteenth century.

34

or less took over because they were far more mobile, particularly in rough or mountainous terrain.

Unfortunately for the poor mules, the men who worked with them had what seems to be an almost universally poor reputation – they made no attempt to understand their mules and treated them very badly. Of course, unsuitable men with no training can be expected to behave like this, and perhaps a large part of the blame lay with their superiors.

Despite, or perhaps because of, this ill-treatment, some amazing feats of endurance are recorded. In August 1857 General Sumner's expedition covered 300 miles from Fort Leavenworth in Kansas Territory via Walnut Creek to Santa Fe in nine days; the hard driving is said to have had very little effect on the mules. In the autumn of 1860, Colonel Riley drove a six-mule team, loaded with 30 cwt, twenty-five days' rations for two men and twelve days' forage for the team (12 lb per mule per day) from Fort Riley in Kansas Territory to Fort Laramie in Nebraska Territory, and then on to Fort Leavenworth; there and back in thirty-eight days of which two and a half days were spent resting – a total of 1,236 miles. Then, after two more days' rest the same team drove to Fort Scott in Kansas Territory – 120 miles in five days, with only a little prairie grass to eat and no hay. No mule lost as much as 10 lb in weight. This demonstrates the mule's stamina and resilience, and the fact that he is fit for plenty of work. Riley had, in 1858, ridden a mule for 1,400 miles in nine weeks. She was completely worn down at the end of the ride, and when he put her in livery he said she was gentle – yet she kicked the ostler viciously. Riley said: 'I have since thought that when a mule gets perfectly gentle he is unfit for service!'

In 1882 a company of scouts and a pack train, loaded with only 200 lb per mule, set out from the San Carlos Agency in Arizona on a three-day forced march covering 280 miles. During the Garza campaign on the Rio Grande that same year a company of the Third Cavalry and another pack train covered 1,078 miles in eighteen days, bettering the record for a day's march set the year before in New Mexico by a pack train that had travelled 85 miles under the desert sun in twelve hours!

General George Custer's campaign into the Black Hills in early 1870 was led on the first day by Buffalo Bill Cody on his little Comanche mule, Mouse. (Incidentally, the Indians, while appreciating the value of mules, never really understood the necessity for big, good quality breeding stock, so their mules were small, if hardy.) He ignored the ridicule he received because he knew Mouse had speed and endurance. Custer told him Mouse was no use, but Cody set off in the lead, and by early afternoon, in terrific heat, the horses were in such a lather that Cody had to stop several times for the column to catch up. Custer was impressed, and tried to swap his fine horse for Mouse; naturally Cody refused. He rode Mouse back that night over the same trail.

Africa and Asia

The South African wars made use of very many mules. Up to the end of 1901 over 67,000 mules (and over 76,000 horses) had been bought from the USA for use in the South African wars. From 1899 to 1902 the average strength of horses and mules employed was about 150,000. The total number of horses used was around 487,000, and mules 147,000, and the incredibly high level of losses (horses 67 per cent, mules 37 per cent), due largely to disease and compounded by lack of organised veterinary care, led to the formation of the Army (now Royal) Veterinary Corps.

Younghusband's expedition which opened up Tibet in 1903 proved a real test for men and animals, the theatre of operations being at an average of 14,000 feet, and as it was winter temperatures of −18 °F were not unusual. There were no roads in the

Enormous numbers of mules served in various capacities in the South African wars. (Photo: Ivan Pascoe.)

barren, rugged country, and 'the mainstay of the transport was our old friend the mule'. One poor mule, after twelve hours up to his neck in a frozen lake, continued his work at once with great zeal the moment he was dragged out.

World War I

The twentieth century saw the beginning of the decline of the mule in both civilian and military spheres in the more highly developed countries. As early as the beginning of World War I primitive motor vehicles were available for military use, but enormous numbers of animals were still needed by all the armies involved.

At the outbreak of war, the British Army had vast knowledge of horses and horse transport, but had to turn to those units who had served in India to make use of their long experience with mules. About half of the total British Army at any one time was serving with the Indian Army, a good deal of this on operations on the rugged Northwest Frontier. Here mules had proved their worth over and over again, and were an integral part of every unit. Since the Indian Mutiny in 1857–1858, there had been the Afghan campaign, almost two years of campaigning in Tibet, and thirty-four noteworthy minor campaigns on the frontier regions of India.

It had quickly become apparent that, if the war expanded, as well as on the main battle front in France many of the new fronts would also require animal transport of some kind, and in particular the mule. Mules were quickly purchased from Canada, North and South America, Spain and Portugal, India and South Africa – between 300,000 and 400,000 were used in total.

Major R. C. H. Berry, writing in the journal of the British Mule Society, gives the numbers of mules at war on 31 August 1918 as shown in the table overleaf. By 31 August 1919 the totals had been reduced to 82 riding mules, 39,644 light draught mules, 37,069 pack mules, and 2,428 unclassified, totalling 79,223.

Perhaps a quarter of a million mules were used on the Western Front, many officers preferring mules to horses for all purposes, one reason being their toughness and powers of resistance to bad conditions, with the added advantage that their length of life at the front was generally considerably longer than that of a horse. They were employed in France on a vast variety of duties supporting the five British armies in the line, and with the advent of the American Army were quickly deployed for their support too.

In Italy a Mule Pack Train Demonstration School was established, for use in the lines of communication up to the two British Army Corps engaged on operations

	Riding	Light draught	Heavy draught	Pack	Un-classified	TOTAL
United Kingdom	–	6,814	587	241	1,163	8,805
France	–	78,665	–	2,395	–	81,060
Italy	–	4,569	–	1,225	–	5,794
Egypt	751	29,560	1,087	10,251	2,279	43,928
Salonika	513	5,632	–	37,838	–	43,983
Mesopotamia	–	27,805	–	16,968	–	44,773
East Africa	–	–	–	–	1,175	1,175
Aden	–	348	–	1,107	–	1,455
TOTAL	1,264	153,393	1,674	70,025	4,617	230,973

Number of mules at war, 31 August 1918

against the Austrians. The mule was totally invaluable in the mountainous terrain of this country, some units in fact only being able to be re-supplied by the use of pack mules.

In Egypt the army played a most significant role throughout the course of the war, providing men, material and animals for virtually all the operations undertaken in the Mediterranean and African campaigns. Its biggest task, though, was support of the British and Australian armies in their drive against the Turks, which eventually ended at Damascus. Some 40,000 mules were used in this theatre of operations, driven by muleteers of many colours and creeds.

Troops in Mesopotamia were almost entirely drawn from the army in India with a good number of British units sprinkled through divisions and brigades as was the custom. Supply lines were lengthy, with most supplies being landed at Basra and then moved on by river until the faithful mule took over for the final stage to the forward troops. Muleteers for the approximately 30,000 mules in this theatre of operations were drawn from, in the main, Indian Army units.

Some 43,000 mules took part in operations in Salonika, led by a variety of muleteers with a large contingent of some 15,000 Greek Cypriots. These were formed into a unit entitled the Macedonian Mule Corps.

An example of the dreadful conditions in which these mules had to work is given in

Army Veterinary Services in the First World War, edited by Major General Blenkinsop and Lt Col. Rainey:

The climate in summer is semi-tropical and the heat of the sun is a force to be reckoned with. The low-lying positions of the country are malarial, and thus disease took its full toll throughout the operations. Biliary fever of horses is a virulent form of enzootic, and has given trouble in the Balkan wars ... very fortunately mules proved immune to this disease. Not a negligible feature of the climate is the high percentage humidity which renders both heat and cold less bearable. There is moreover a remarkable variety of climate hardly less trying. To give an example: on December 1st 1917 the maximum temperature at a typical station was as high as 65 °F and the minimum 40 °F, while less than a week later the maximum temperature was at zero and the minimum was 13° of frost. During the first winter both horses and mules suffered considerably from 'chill'. They had landed with heavy coats, and it was impossible to clip them owing to the failure in the supply of clipping machines. It was a common thing for them to be wet through when working and then to be chilled to the bone by the cutting winds. On the lines of communication, where the work was very heavy, whole companies at a time were affected in this way. Pneumonia on this front was unknown, as the animals lived always in the open.

A nice story of man's debt to the mule is told by Percy Tomlin in the journal of the British Mule Society. Serving in Salonika in January 1917 his unit received 135 unbroken mules direct from Argentina, and set out to break them. He and one particular mule, Daisy, took a liking to each other. One day he was on light duties (through having been kicked by another mule!) and was given the job of escorting some camels and their drivers back to Shellal Dump, following a 'wire road' – not a real road, but slats of wire placed in the sand to mark the route, which was difficult to follow, particularly in the dark. On his way back alone, in pitch darkness, to where they had bivouacked for the first time the previous night, he accidentally got off the route without realising it. After a while Daisy stopped dead, and despite all his efforts refused to be pushed on. As he got off to find out why, the moon came out from behind the clouds – and he found they were on the brink of a high cliff. After hugging Daisy, he climbed back on, and this time gave her her head, as she obviously had more sense than he had. She took him straight back to the bivouac.

At the end of the war, the vast majority of the mules which had survived were sold off. By 31 March 1920 there were only the following numbers of mules in the army:

UK	2,812
France	918
Army of the Rhine	975
Army of the Black Sea	3,294
Mesopotamia	26,656
Total	34,655

Mules were offered to the public at an average price of £36.10.8, compared to £37.3.3 for horses and £9.1.6 for donkeys.

So despite the incredible job they did throughout the war, the numbers of British Army mules were reduced to a very few, as many people believed that with advancing mechanisation, animal transport would no longer be needed. Luckily, one animal transport company was retained for training junior officers in riding, horsemastership and pack transport duties, should they be called upon to organise this in an emergency.

However, in India, where animals had always been appreciated, and were still used by army and civilians alike, mule numbers were still high – in India in 1929 the army had over 24,000 horses, 26,000 mules, 13,000 cattle and 5,000 camels. These were used as much as anywhere on the Northwest Frontier, where skirmishes were still taking place.

The Mountain Artillery

Probably the best-known military use of mules is by the Mountain Artillery on India's Northwest Frontier, where they carried the 'screw guns' made famous by Kipling.

The first-known mention of Mountain Artillery was in the Peninsular War of 1813, but the 'genuine' Mountain Batteries, with pack mules and Indian Gunners, were set up in India in 1841, where they served with distinction in heavy fighting in Afghanistan. They were disbanded in 1843, but their performance had been so impressive that the first permanent British Mountain Battery took part in the Bhutan campaign of 1864–1865 and the Abyssinian campaign of 1869. The first screw gun was introduced in 1879. Development of Mountain Artillery was stimulated by the Second Afghan War of 1879–1880 when Lord Roberts took two British Mountain

Batteries and one Indian Mountain Battery on his celebrated march from Kabul to Kandahar. Their success led to each division of the army in India having three Mountain Batteries before the end of the century for service beyond the Frontier.

From 1918 the Mountain Batteries' main armament was the 3.7-inch howitzer, carried in parts on the backs of eight mules which, in order of march, were: first mule – carriage; second mule – wheels and axle; third mule – pivot; fourth mule – cradle; fifth mule – trail legs; sixth mule – shield and slipper; seventh mule – breach; eighth mule – chase. Each Mountain Battery had (in theory) 102 mules: the Gun Line had thirty-two (eight mules for each of four guns) plus twenty-four to carry the ammunition; the Relief Line had sixteen (to take over from any which needed to be relieved of its load for any reason), and other equipment was carried by thirty more mules. There were also thirteen Royal Indian Army Service Corps first-line mules attached if these were available. Almost always there were fewer mules than this,

Indian Army Mountain Artillery mule carrying wheels and axle of a screw gun (photographed in 1940, but virtually unchanged for around 100 years). (Photo: Capt. Dick Ashby.)

which put far more pressure on all the mules. They were 14.2 to 15 hh and heavily built, having to carry some very heavy weights – up to 444 lb including saddlery for one of the ammunition mules.

The animals needed to be strong not only because of the heavy weights, but because of the extremely harsh climate and difficult terrain with which they usually had to cope. Many of us now appreciate this, having seen much film of Afghanistan and Pakistan on television in recent years. To carry such heavy weights straight up steep hillsides, often at great speed and in blizzards, requires great strength and determination. Having reached the place where the guns were needed, on the command 'Action front' men and mules took up their positions. The Gunners off-loaded the gun parts and assembled them, then off-loaded the leather ammunition boxes, two of which, each containing four rounds, were carried by each ammunition mule. The guns were then quickly assembled. Everything was done with such skill and speed that from the order to firing a shell, ideally, not more than one minute had elapsed!

The Mountain Gunners were very proud of their capabilities, and of their mules, and many tales are told of their exploits, most of the following being taken from *Tales of the Mountain Gunners*. Major J. P. Warren, who with Lt Col. C. H. T. MacFetridge edited the book, said: 'There was nothing more stirring to behold than a column of Mountain Artillery on the move, men and animals marching for mile after mile at a pace even the Light Infantry found difficult to keep up with, despite the heavy loads on the backs of the magnificent Mountain Artillery mules.'

It was the boast of the Mountain Artillery that 'they could go anywhere a man could go without using his hands'. They could also cover long distances in a short time when necessary. Pat Carmichael tells of a march of 53 miles in seventeen hours (including a three-hour halt), the first section through the worst part of a very hot day, the latter section at night through a forest.

Major-General B. Daunt, CB, CBE, DSO praised the mule's common sense, telling of the time when some mules and horses escaped their drivers and galloped round the camp, some inevitably becoming entangled in coils of old barbed wire. One horse went mad, plunging and lashing about and cutting his legs to pieces. The two mules stopped immediately, stood still, looked all round them, extricated themselves carefully, leg by leg, without a scratch and then continued gambolling around in the joy of being free.

He was also one of many who appreciated the mule's sense of humour. His favourite, very gentle mule had been allocated to a nervous young recruit for grooming, but the young man was making heavy weather of lifting the mule's hind feet to pick out the hooves. Daunt, full of confidence, stepped up and demonstrated, running his hand over the mule's quarters, down to the fetlock, lifting the leg quietly and laying it inside his thigh: 'See,' he said, after he had picked out the hoof, 'you don't even have to hold it with your hands, it just lies in your thigh.' The mule then took his hoof off Daunt's thigh, placed it gently against his bottom and pushed him so that he fell on his face behind the mule, 'unhurt but discomfited'. He felt this was a gentle reproof for showing off, and 'gave the mule lines a good laugh in the still of the night when they chew one another's rugs and discuss the news of the day'.

Daunt, incidentally, although he loved horses, admitted that in many ways the mule was cleverer and better balanced psychologically. He also said that although it was true that mules have a wider kicking range with their hind feet than horses, particularly forward ('I've heard a mule described as being able to mount herself!'), among the 200 mules of his acquaintance, he only knew two which were dangerous, and one of those was 'only ticklish and perhaps a little suspicious of man's intentions'.

Many people have demonstrated the mule's intelligence with stories of their recognition of the signal for 'Feed up' at important moments. M. D. Bell in *The Gunner*, the journal of the Mountain Artillery, tells of a time in the desert of Mesopotamia in World War II, when during the brief rainy period, grass suddenly appeared everywhere, and after morning stables the whole mule strength was turned out of camp to graze. There was some apprehension when they all instantly disappeared into the blue, but when both trumpeters sounded 'Feed' and 'Water', every mule appeared within a very few moments, and as each came in it took up its own place in the standings.

Another occasion on which Gunners were relieved and somewhat surprised to see their mules return is reported by Lt Col. M. F. Kemmis Betty. In Waziristan the deep dry nullahs (river beds) offered very good cover, so when a camp had such a nullah snaking through it, practically the whole camp was set up within it – thousands of animals, dozens of cookhouses, messes and so on. During the night the rains came; very quickly the dry nullah was filled with a rushing torrent. The men grabbed what they could and ran. The horses and mules pulled up their picketing pegs, scrambled out and kept going. Evacuation continued through the night, but there was no point in looking for the animals until dawn. 'The happy ending throws an interesting light on the different natures of horse and mule. Speaking for my Battery, I can swear that whereas it took the whole of the next day to round up the last of our panic-stricken horses, every single mule was back in his place in time for the morning nosebag!'

Brigadier Munn tells of a cunning mule who would stand in the lines with its head in the manger, apparently asleep, until someone passed between the lines of mangers, when he would raise his head, take a lightning nip out of their backside, and have his head back in the manger by the time they could look round! He also tells a story typical of mules: in 1934 a Mountain Battery was marching up from the Plains to the Simla Hills when a mule was pushed over the edge of a steep hillside. It rolled right down, with its legs neatly tucked in as it rolled over and over. Although the saddle was ruined, the mule was fine – it got up, shook itself and carried on with its duty. Many similar stories are told of mules, with the comment that under similar circumstances horses would have struggled and probably broken a leg, making them useless – a great loss to the men.

As Lt Col. MacFetridge relates, an Indian Officer in Burma had told the men that the mules, not the guns, were the most valuable possession of the battery – they took seven years to grow, be trained and become capable of carrying a gun-load or eight shells, whereas guns could be replaced from Rawalpindi Arsenal within a week, and furthermore dropped from the air! Mules must not be lost at any cost. The drivers were terrified of the consequences if they lost their mules, and would go to any lengths to ensure that this did not happen.

A. Y. Arledge wrote of the mule's

genius of self-preservation; it will skirt the brink of a cliff etc. with the care and sure-footedness of a goat; will discover hidden dangers far quicker than man; his superior intelligence enables him to know when a bog is miry or when quicksand is about without having to step into it; his ears give warning to man of a person or animal about, he can detect a snake in the grass or person lying in wait.

A mule sees and hears more than a horse, is ever on the alert, is difficult to stampede, and makes a good sentry. Arledge continues: 'The mule will speak out and tell you a thousand things that a horse will let pass without saying a word' (*The Mule*).

J. K. Kendall (Dum-Dum), a Mountain Gunner, in 'Tales of the Border', writes:

The mountains of Baluchistan are, as ground for marching over, particularly unpleasant. The 'going' is mainly over loose stones; there is no shade, practically no water, and to all intents and purposes you make your path as you go along . . . we started one morning before dawn and marched under such conditions, up and down, down and up, until about 3.30 pm.

The guns got there! One mule only fell out:

44

She marched on, hour after hour, and finally fainted away with the load on her back . . . And there is your pig-headed obstinacy. Now this was not an isolated case. The only difference between her and her companions in misfortune was that she happened to faint and they did not.

He also paid this glowing tribute to the mule:

It is as a mountaineer that the mule shines . . . some of the problems the mules solved . . . were of a nature to make the hair stand on end . . . The weight carried is great, ranging as it used to from 260 lb to 360 lb; the ease with which impossibilities are achieved is ridiculous; and the philosophic coolness with which a mule will stand, with all his four feet close together, perched on a pinnacle of nothingness, and thence determine the next downward step into the void, is a study of cheerfulness and sound sense under difficulties to which I know no parallel. He never loses his head. He never seems to want to turn back. He does not get frightened at prospective perils. He knows exactly what is wanted of him, and literally brings his mind to bear on each emergency as it comes up.

Major J. Nettlefield, MC, obviously impressed with the mule's stoicism, tells a story which he describes as a 'fantasy based on fact'. In Burma, behind Japanese lines, a party had been laying out a line to the summit of a ridge, and were on their way back down the jungle track. Shots rang out in front of them from a Japanese platoon. The men jumped into the bed of a nullah at the side of the track, but could not drag the mules with them because of the very steep sides and very thick undergrowth. One mule, seeing the Japanese and their guns blocking his way, 'put his head down and charged, kicking up his heels in a show of rage which surprised even himself'. When the men emerged at the bottom of the ridge, they did not expect ever to see the mule again – but there he was quietly grazing! Back at the Battery position an officer looked the mule over, and found a bullet hole through his neck just below his mane. It did not look serious, and as his saddle was still in place, he was detailed for a full load and marched all that night.

The next day, when he was unsaddled, his driver came to rub him down – and found a long slit in the mule's side from which pus was already beginning to ooze. The bullet had penetrated the saddle exactly between the panel and the blanket, leaving nothing to show on the outside, and had finished up in his ribs, fracturing one. 'But during that long trying march he had carried his heavy load without a murmur – and on his face was his usual vacuous look.'

45

A final story of the Mountain Artillery mules illustrates the mule's great sense of self-preservation which the army found so useful. Lt Col. C. C. M. McLeod-Carey, on a journey through the Himalayas, was travelling along the Hindustan-Tibet road 'which was becoming rather hazardous in places . . . Here we learned a lot about the wisdom of that sagacious animal the mule'. Some stretches of the 'road' were very narrow, with big rocks sticking out on one side and a sheer drop on the other of two to three thousand feet. Their large Mountain Battery mules 'were too broad in the beam for this kind of going. They knew a thing or two and would flatly refuse to budge if they thought their side loads might touch any rock that would force their hind legs to slide out over the edge.' Once off-loaded, the mules would go through the narrow part, while the men carried the loads to a suitable point for re-loading.

In World War I the Artillery was by far the major user of horses and mules (not the cavalry), and in World War II it used very many mules in all theatres of war, doing a wonderful variety of invaluable work.

World War II

As the threat of war grew once more, some armies, such as the German and Italian, realised the value of pack transport, and began to reorganise pack transport units, but the British Army, as at the beginning of World War I, had no such units. Once again the need for animal transport became clear, despite the existence of sophisticated mechanised transport, and once again the British Army turned to India, this time in the shape of the Royal Indian Army Service Corps, for help. The Indian Army responded swiftly, sending 2,700 mules with their drivers to join the British Expeditionary Force in France, and in total providing 26,000 mules.

It has proved remarkably difficult to find any comprehensive figures for the number of mules used in World War II, largely, I assume, because they were used by all the armies involved, being purchased in many different places and sent to all the various theatres of war. Far fewer horses were used than in World War I, and fewer mules also, but many more mules than horses – perhaps 100,000–150,000. The following may at least give some idea of the part mules played.

Northwest Europe

In October 1939 it had been decided that the British Expeditionary Force (BEF) would need fifty pack animals to each frontline division to carry ammunition and supplies to forward positions where approaches had been made impassable to wheeled traffic by heavy shelling. India provided four fully equipped Animal Transport Companies and a remount unit and mules for two Cypriot Pack Transport units – a total strength of about 2,700 animals. By the end of January 1940 they were at work and widely distributed with BEF. Despite severe winter weather, the Indian mules did well and the sick rate was never over 2.4 per cent, although there were few facilities for roughing their shoes by means of frost nails, and they slipped badly on the frozen pavé of the French roads.

When the German blitzkrieg started, one company was captured in May 1940, the others withdrawing to Dunkirk and St Nazaire, but the mules could not be evacuated because the ships could not be spared for them.

Between 1941 and 1943 army horses and mules in the UK reached a peak of 5,450, partly because it was thought that Pack Transport and Mountain Batteries might be needed in Norway, and partly to save petrol in the UK. They were trained in Wales and Scotland for possible work in the cold mountainous country of Norway, but of course in the event they were never needed there. In January 1942, incidentally, the sick rate was 7.8 per cent for horses and only 2.8 per cent for mules, an indication of their comparative hardiness.

The campaign in Northwest Europe in 1944–1945 did not use many equines: two Mountain Regiments, Royal Artillery, with mules from the USA, six Indian Army and four Royal Army Service Corps pack companies, the latter being issued with surplus cavalry horses and cobs bought in the UK and a Norwegian contingent. The total was only around 3,700 animals.

Middle East

In September 1940 the 27th Mountain Battery, Royal Artillery, was sent from India to Aden with 175 mules and 30 horses. The Jammu and Kashmir Mountain Battery was originally to go to Aden also, but was instead sent to the Sudan and took part in the Eritrean campaign. Some thousands of mules were employed in carrying arms and supplies from the Sudan to aid the rebellion against the Italians in Abyssinia, but it was not until the 4th and 3rd Indian Divisions had the enemy at bay in an immensley strong natural defensive position at Keren that organised pack units were needed.

Numbers 1 and 2 Cypriot Pack Transport Companies, RASC, after their escape from France earlier in the year, had been re-equipped in Egypt with 800 hinnies bought in Cyprus. After a short training period they were taken up the Nile by cattle barges to Wadi Halfa, and then by rail to the Eritrean border. They then marched across country for twelve days to Keren through arid bush country. The Kashmir and Jammu Mountain Battery was, at the same time, marching up.

Arriving in February 1941 these units set to work at once to supply the forward positions and to build up dumps for the attack, climbing two or three times daily about 2,000 feet up precipitous hills, sometimes under shell fire, often at night. By the end of the action about 200 enemy mules had been captured, of which about seventy could be patched up sufficiently to replace Allied casualties. Shortage of shoes and casualties among farriers meant that many mules became foot-sore, and saddle galls were a problem because they had no rest. As soon as the campaign was over they returned to Egypt as they had come – on foot, by rail and by ship. Only seventeen mules were lost to disease (probably African Horse Sickness), the rest arrived in excellent condition, even fat.

Feats of endurance of this kind – for men as well as mules – were quite common, and were repeated many times in similar vein throughout the theatres of war.

The French Army in Syria, incidentally, was not very highly mechanised, and many thousands of animals were used under pack, principally mules. After the campaign against the Vichy French in Syria the British Army took over 1,200 horses and 3,200 mules. By October 1942 2,800 horses and mules were in transport companies. Also in the Middle East were six Cypriot Pack Transport Companies, fifteen Indian mule companies and one Mountain Artillery patrol; a total of over 6,500 horses, 9,600 mules and 1,700 camels.

Further figures for mule movements are given by Clabby. In 1942 more than 1,000 mules were sent from the Middle East to India by ship, with few casualties despite the heat, rough seas and unsuitable ships, and thanks to the excellent care they received. Between 7 October and 28 November 1942, seven Indian mule companies and one Mountain Battery marched cross country from Syria to Iraq, a total of 370 miles, with only a 0.78 per cent casualty rate. From 31 December 1943 to March 1945, 493 horses and 12,458 mules were sent from Alexandria, Port Said, Haifa and Beirut in twenty-one contingents to Palestine and Syria, the mortality rate en route being 1.46 per cent in horses and 0.15 per cent in mules.

North Africa

When the Anglo-American invasion of North Africa took place in November 1942, ships were scarce and only two Pack Transport companies were landed – they had stores and saddlery, but were brought up to full numbers with locally requisitioned mules. (Out of 20,000 examined in Tunisia and Algeria, only 922 pack mules and forty-five riding horses were considered suitable.) For the first few weeks they had little to do, but then, as the action warmed up, the weather cooled down; very cold, very wet weather was hardly what was expected in North Africa. Even the tanks became bogged down and mule transport was called for urgently.

Brigadier Clabby says:

> The two companies acquitted themselves well in the operations preceding the final offensive which took place in mountainous country covered with dense scrub while all the time rain fell in torrents. In one instance pack transport was used, perhaps for the first time, to supply tank crews with rations, and in areas unfit for motor transport, mule cacolets and litters were employed for the evacuation of wounded men.

The Germans had used pack transport on a considerable scale, but by the end most animals had been lost, stolen or eaten. About 250 horses and mules were captured by the Allies.

Italy

The mules used in North Africa were left behind when the 8th Army sailed to Sicily in July 1943 and on to Italy at the beginning of September, but saddlery and equipment were taken and locally captured mules were used. Later, 678 horses and mules were brought over from Tunisia, having sat in the harbour for eight days before sailing. David Limpus tells of these mules taking part in a number of amphibious operations in which the mules showed their adaptability by causing no problems when embarking or disembarking from small open boats, and by adapting so quickly to strict army discipline and hard work.

More mules were bought in Southern Italy; the 8th Army bought 951 mules and 46 horses. At Catania 500 mules per month were purchased from October 1943 onwards. More pack mules were shipped with their units from Syria, Palestine and Egypt. In all, around 10,000 animals, the vast majority mules, were collected, many of which needed training. A good allowance had to be made for the purchase of further mules to cover wastage because there was a shortage of pack saddles, and of trained men, which meant losses would be higher than usual, although the local mules themselves were mostly of excellent quality.

At first there was little demand for pack transport because the land was flat and easy for motor vehicles, but as the Allies drove the Germans northwards, and the terrain became more mountainous, pack transport was in great demand. The units often travelled to wherever they were needed by road – four mules, two muleteers and all their equipment in a 3-ton lorry.

David Limpus wrote: 'Cassino was the worst engagement. Mules could only work at night, the enemy having the advantage of the highest ground and observing every movement by day. We lost many mules and some personnel at this time.' Once again the mules were used throughout a wet winter to carry ammunition and supplies to the crews of tanks bogged down in the mud. David Limpus says that throughout the campaign 30,000 mules were involved, consisting of 4 Pack Group, the Cypriot Group, the RIASC companies, the Royal Artillery Mountain Regiment with their large mules and Basuto muleteers, and of course the French Division under General Juin, who eventually got round the abbey at Monte Cassino by going straight across country, completely dependent on the mules for supplies, weapons, ammunition and so on. Later, Italian companies were formed into a group commanded by British officers. The US 5th Army also had a number of large Texan mules.

By March 1945, purchasing had almost stopped and mules were being moved to India ready for the Burma campaign. By 10 May 1945, 3,500 Animal Transport and 580 Mountain Artillery mules had been selected for transfer to India. Many others were needed in North Italy, and others went to UNRRA for relief work in Greece, and to Yugoslavia.

The official history of the Italian campaign includes the following statement: 'The Italian campaign is the only one in which considerable numbers of pack and other animal transport were used . . . It is impossible to say that armies in future will not find themselves fighting in areas where motor transport must be supplemented by pack transport.' I would, however, argue with the above statement that this was the only such campaign.

Tylden adds:

> The Army had learnt to appreciate the many virtues of the mule during the fighting in the mountains in Italy and though the second World War had been the first of the wars in which mechanisation had played a really tremendous role, it did leave the British Army a memory of the virtues of the animals which had

Indian Army transport cart Mk VII, 1944. (Photo: Major Philip Malins.)

served past generations so faithfully and well. In all some 85,000 animals were handed over by the German Army when the final surrender took place.

It was in Italy, incidentally, that another story is told, by Major J. C. Ratcliffe, of mules' reaction to the signal for 'Feed' – but this one is unique. When the king was visiting the troops in a jeep, the wagon lines of the Mountain Regiment in which Major Ratcliffe was serving were ordered, with their mules, to line the hilly and rough route – not to stand rigidly to attention, but to cheer as the king passed. 'As the Royal Party approached, an intelligent NCO sounded "Feed". The response from the mules was overwhelming, and the King, at first visibly alarmed, was then highly amused at what must surely have been the loudest cheering he heard that day.'

India

In India up until the end of 1941 little use was made of animal transport. At the outbreak of war the numbers of animals in the army there were the same as in 1929

51

(see p. 40). Some animal transport companies were sent to France in 1939 and 620 mules were sent in the spring of 1940. Animals were also sent to the Sudan and Aden in 1940 and mules to the Middle East in 1941; also in 1941 mule and camel companies were sent to Iraq.

From 1942 it became clear that the war was beginning to swing towards the Far East, and that more animal transport would be needed there. Instead of providing mules for other theatres of war, India now had to build up her own numbers. Some were purchased locally (although many people believed these to be inferior to the imported mules); between 1943 and 1945 nearly 7,000 were sent from the USA; and from South Africa between 1942 and 1945 more than 22,000 mules were shipped to India, principally for use by the Chindits in Burma.

W. Gale served with 3rd Field Brigade, Royal Artillery in India, and gives an example of the mule's ability. An 18-pound gun was stuck cradle-deep in a mid-river sand bank, and sixteen horses, in two teams of six and one team of four, had tried to pull it out but had failed and given up. A mere seven mules, one in front with three pairs behind, put their full weight into their breast collars, re-positioned their feet immediately they felt a slackening of the traces, maintaining the pull at all times – and the job was done. But Gale says, they would never tackle anything they knew was impossible or might hurt them.

Burma

Probably the most famous use of mules in World War II was by the Chindits – Orde Wingate's Long Range Penetration Force set up to penetrate behind Japanese lines in Burma to cut their lines of communication. About 550 horses and nearly 3,500 mules were used in Burma.

Because of the conditions (in particular the dense jungle) and because of the need to keep weight down when flying in, small mules were chosen of 10.2 to 12.2 hh, of good conformation, sound with good strong legs, particularly in the forehand. The 10.2–11 hh mules carried up to 160 lb, the 11–12.2 hh mules 200 lb upwards.

The mules arriving at the training base at Jullundur in India were largely unbroken and unhandled, and some were very wild, having been shipped for many weeks to reach India. They were trained here in a matter of four weeks or less, which barely allowed time to get them really fit and hardened off, before they were sent to the various units, where they had little time to accustom themselves to the job in hand before setting off for Burma.

Mule being loaded for a flight into Burma, 1944. (Photo: Reg Rimmer.)

Before leaving for Burma the mules had to be de-voiced lest their very penetrating calls should give them, and the men with them, away to the Japanese. A simple operation was devised of removing the vocal chords; one man could de-voice thirty mules a day. Of 5,563 animals de-voiced in India, there were only forty-three casualties. A few mules did regain their voices, or something like them, in time, but most did not.

From Jullundur the units moved to Assam, and from there into Burma, either on foot or by air. This was the first time that animals had been flown in to an operational base.

Altogether, 2,216 animals were flown in to three air strips – 'Aberdeen', 'White City' and 'Broadway' – carved out of the jungle on the advanced strongholds of the Chindits deep in enemy-occupied territory. The journey of approximately 300 miles was carried out by C-47 Douglas Army Transport aeroplanes, each of them towing two gliders. The planes were modified by having coconut matting on the floor and bamboo poles providing separate compartments for each mule: three animals across in two rows, plus their drivers and gear. The gliders carried three animals well forward, immediately against the backs of the pilot and co-pilot – the first and third mules facing the rear (their hind feet uncomfortably close to the pilots' heads) and the second mule facing forward, where he could look over the pilots' shoulders and give them advice! The planes were flown by both the RAF and No. 1 Air Commando of the USAF, with great skill and courage.

Loading had to be carried out in the dark, but was so well organised that mules could be loaded at the rate of one a minute. There were few problems in loading or in flight, the only major one being when four mules broke loose in flight and had to be shot, but landing, particularly for the gliders, was a different matter. John Masters wrote:

> The glider pilots had a difficult task landing on the makeshift air strips . . . This one landed in the exact centre of the strip, and going the right way; but when he reached the end he was still doing 40 mph. Again the horrible splintering and the pistol-shot crack of boughs as the wide-winged beast plunged into the thicket at the end of the strip . . . – after five minutes we found it, on its back, a twisted mass of wreckage . . . A British private climbed out, said, 'F— ' without emphasis, and turned to help us. One by one five other soldiers and an officer followed, each making the same comment. Finally we dragged out the mules. Being devocalised they could not say anything, but one of them tried to bite me in the arm, and I don't blame him.

In case relief mules were needed where no airstrip was possible, thought was given to the possibility of dropping mules by parachute. Major K. I. Barlow, RAVC was given responsibility for devising a method, and trials were carried out at Chaklala, India. The mules, lightly sedated, each sat on an inflatable dinghy mounted on a 6½ by 4 foot wooden platform, surrounded by pontoons on all sides and above to protect them from injury. Seven live drops were carried out, the mules being ejected at 600 feet, and they all landed quite safely. Despite the success, this method was little used.

Behind Japanese lines, life was very hard for both men and mules. They received regular supply drops by air – a risky undertaking for the pilots – but had to stay on duty week after week when other troops would have been relieved. For the first six weeks the mules put on condition, unlike the ponies who lost condition, and became very fit, but food was a real problem, with no grain for much of the time, although the mules did better than the ponies on what was available, even eating bamboo leaves. The mules suffered from many diseases of the foot and skin, from colic, from surra (although not as frequently as the horses) and occasionally from tetanus and piroplasmosis. Injuries were an even bigger problem. Because of the lack of spare animals, deterioration of the saddlery, difficult loads, long marches with little rest, overloading and sometimes inexperienced handlers, saddle sores were very common. Pat Carmichael writes:

> It was painful to a mule with a sore back just to put a saddle on him. It hurt us all and especially the drivers to have to do it and then to see the gun loaded on as well. Admiration for our mules had always been enormous. Now, seeing the true extent of their steadiness and patience and their continuing endurance, it was boundless. Men developed close relationships with their mules – they could often be heard at night squatting or lying near their tethered mules, talking quietly to them.

Indeed there are many examples of men loving their mules so much that they gave up their own water or chance of a truck ride for the sake of their mules.

Other injuries were received from shells, bombs, grenades, splinters and so on, from the sharp and often poisonous vegetation, and to the feet – although the unshod mules suffered less than the ponies which needed shoeing, as shoes were in short supply. The heat, humidity and mountainous terrain exhausted the mules, particularly when they were unable to get the rest they needed and enough food. In five months of jungle fighting behind Japanese lines animal casualties amounted to 273 horses (50 per cent) and 1,169 mules (37 per cent).

The type of work carried out by the mules is illustrated by a march undertaken by 63rd Brigade from Tiddim to Imphal when they covered twenty-seven miles in twenty-four hours. On the journey water was found only once, the going was very bad and the mules were under load for periods of twelve hours and seven hours. Despite this there was no increase in girth galls although they lost condition because of the hard work and poor rations.

One of the tasks which mules had to tackle was crossing rivers, many of which were very wide, deep and fast-flowing. Various methods have been tried of taking large parties of mules across rivers, including loading them into boats or on to rafts, towing them behind boats, and swimming them tied up or free. The River Irrawaddy in

Chindit mules approaching the 'Blackpool' stronghold in Burma. (Photo: Major Frank Turner.)

Burma was one of the more difficult to cross, particularly as it was behind Japanese lines and the men were continually under threat of attack. Major Frank Turner, Animal Transport Officer with 111 Indian Infantry Brigade, tells of the time when they had to cross this river, a mile wide, with 240 horses and mules. The mules refused to swim the river, so one man, Mike MacGillicuddy, mounted a horse bareback and led a group of fifteen animals into the water, a few ridden by good swimmers, the others on their own. His horse reached the deep water and began to swim, and although the mules had always swum well in training, now, when it mattered, most of them refused to follow him, but turned downstream and let the current take them back to their original shore. The rest of the mules had refused even to start. After trying this several times without success, MacGillicuddy mounted

Maggy, the biggest mule they had, who carried the heaviest load; and the most precious – the radio set. With an assault boat forcibly towing two other mules by their head ropes, twenty mules made the crossing. Meanwhile Major Turner had got another batch started, but these turned back almost from midstream. Men in a small boat leant out over the gunwales dragging mules behind them. MacGillicuddy and Maggy swam back and forth across the mile of fast-flowing river, with small groups following them – the mules seemed to trust her. By the time it became dark and mules could no longer be persuaded to enter the water – not all had been got across and some had to be left behind – MacGillicuddy and Maggy had made ten crossings!

Incidentally, Lt Col. MacFetridge tells me that mules were trained to swim across a river by having their food taken to the other side and 'Feed' sounded. The mules' response to this signal again came in very useful.

Maggy proved her worth again when Captain Hanley of the King's Own had his skull cracked by 'flying fruit' (the nickname invented for any load dropped from an aeroplane – food, equipment etc. – since one poor man had been hit by a can of pineapple). He was in a very poor way, and needed to be evacuated, but when they tried taking him to a cleared strip three miles back to be evacuated by air, the first plane cracked up on landing, and the second, with the unconscious Hanley aboard, cracked up on take-off, slamming him head-first against the forward wall of the cabin. He was brought back to the rest of the party and had to be taken with them. A type of travois was rigged up from two bamboo poles, placed either side of Maggy with the thick ends fastened to her saddle, the thin ends trailing behind her on the ground. Across these were fastened two short pieces of bamboo, one just above her tail and another six feet lower down. Two double blankets were fastened into this rectangle into which Hanley was secured with another blanket. Maggy carried and towed Hanley for five days for a distance of about fifty miles to a place where he could be picked up by plane, and during that period she never kicked, bucked or slipped, despite the awkward 'load', and even on the worst ground, and she never even mucked when Hanley was in place.

John Masters, who witnessed this, says:

> I will swear that she knew what she was doing, and although I am not unduly fond of any animals except cats, more than once I found myself, at night, hugging Maggy round the neck, stroking her and whispering into her ear what a good, brave and clever girl she was . . . beautiful, too, I would add, remembering her sex. She snickered coyly.

Delhi Victory Parade, 1945: 15 Mountain Battery marching up Kingsway. A representation of Mountain Artillery with composite sections to show the different peoples from India (Sikhs and Punjabi Mussulmans) who served in the Mountain Artillery. Each row of mules is carrying a part of a screw gun. 1st row – carriage, 2nd row – wheels and axle, 3rd row – pivot, 4th row – trail legs, 5th row – gun barrels, etc. (Photo: Major Philip Malins.)

Hanley was, you will be pleased to hear, picked up by the USAF and survived. Maggy, sadly, came to a far less happy end. John Masters went to the mule lines one evening and found Maggy quietly eating bamboo, a red gash in her belly and her entrails hanging out. She seemed to him to be in no pain. With great sadness he ordered her to be shot at once. Many other mules died from their wounds or disease, and some came to a very important but rather inglorious end: when the men were

close to starvation, exhausted and disease-ridden and some wounded, it was sometimes necessary to kill one of the mules to make stew to keep the men alive.

Henry Kirk gives an example of the sterling work done by mules, at the siege of Imphal in April 1944. (This was a terrible affair with 12,603 British and Commonwealth casualties and 54,879 Japanese.) They had to climb 'Nightmare Peak', which rose to 5,038 feet, part of the defences of the all-weather airstrip of

Kangla on the valley floor. It was a very dangerous operation to reach the peak, as it was jungle-covered and very steep. The rocky ledges had just enough room for a mule and its pack, with a drop of hundreds of feet over the edge, and the company was under fire. In nine weeks Kirk and his fellows and their mules completed 187 round trips with supplies, water, food, ammunition and so on. 'Our duo [of mules] got to know every step of the route. We used to give them their heads and walk behind holding onto their tails, chatting to them, their ears standing up like goal posts.' These mules were the lifeline to 140 men, but the conditions in which they worked were atrocious, very hot and humid. 'Their courage and resilience saw us through, they won the hearts of many Burma veterans, and in that campaign earned their rightful place in the history of it.'

Post-World War II

All the mules and other animals belonging to and captured by the allied armies had to be disposed of, through liaison with governments and various other bodies. Many were given or sold to local farmers so that agriculture could return to normal as quickly as possible, as happened, for example, in Greece. In some countries, particularly the Middle East and North Africa, previous unpleasant experiences of the treatment meted out to ex-army animals meant that none were sold locally. From northwest Europe some were shipped to England and sold by auction in small batches. In the Far East most of the mules and other animals were shot, because shipment to Europe was too expensive, and local disposal seemed unwise. Many tears are said to have been shed throughout the Far East as men said goodbye to mules who had shared their trials and tribulations and to whom many owed their lives.

Clabby says that at one period the British Army alone had 120,000 animals plus 80,000 horses and mules captured from the enemy in Europe, but by 1946 this number was already down to 27,000.

One of the few public tributes paid to mules was the inclusion of a Mountain Battery in the New Delhi Victory Parade. Mountain Gunners always felt that their beloved mules never received the recognition they deserved in Britain. At long last a memorial to the Chindits and their mules has recently been erected in London.

Korea

Mules have been used in many conflicts since World War II, and in particular they were found useful in Korea. The US Army did not have its own mules, and the lack of availability of mules in the early days was very keenly felt. Col. R. E. Ireland, former cavalry officer and Chief of the Remount Service, wrote:

> The absence of pack troops in Korea was due to the non-availability in the US of trained organisations. Had there been, their value can be estimated by the fact that, without exception, all the horses and mules captured from the Chinese and North Koreans, by the use of enemy or improvised equipment, were utilised for pack transport if they were physically able to carry a load, for example in the mountainous sector north of Seoul to the Imjin River, captured animals were used to pack in barbed wire, steel stakes, mines etc.

Amazingly, several of the captured mules turned out to be ex-US Army mules which had been commandeered by the Red Chinese Army in the China–Burma–India conflict.

Today and tomorrow

The last troop of mules in the British Army was disbanded in Hong Kong in 1976, and the US Army took mules out of service at West Point in 1972 – although West Point still has a mule as its mascot. The passing of the mules was, in both cases, not effected without great sadness from even the most hardened of soldiers. However, many armies still have pack-mule units, principally those countries where in civilian life mechanisation is incomplete and mules are still widely used, such as India and Pakistan and many South American countries. Several other countries where mechanisation is otherwise almost complete, such as Italy, Switzerland and Spain, still maintain pack-mule units, particularly appreciating the values of mules in their own mountainous areas.

The British Army now sees no need for mules, as virtually its only work has been in Germany and Northern Ireland where the countryside is generally flat and mechanised transport – including helicopters – can be used for the work, which is mainly patrolling. However, the Falklands conflict brought the mule back into people's thoughts. Mules could have carried the heavy equipment of the men who 'yomped' across rough country to Port Stanley and thus left the men fitter for the battle – and also better equipped, because more could have been carried. Once hostilities were over and re-building began, mules could have been used instead of

'Trotter', the US Military Academy (West Point) mascot, showing a weapons load, July 1967. (US Army.)

helicopters to carry materials and supplies across the roadless miles of rough country, the helicopters not only being very expensive, but also limited by the bad weather. In fact, following a letter in *The Times* from the author, pack equipment was flown out from the UK to be used on local ponies. Also, in addition to the existing equitation course undertaken by all Royal Army Veterinary Corps recruits, which includes the basics of pack transport, a new course was set up for officers, mainly in the Royal Corps of Transport, to ensure that, should a pack unit be needed in future, it could be set up quickly using local animals and equipment. In the past, of course, this technique has rarely been successful, as the local animals and saddlery were often of poor quality – if available at all.

A wonderful example of the value of mules for military campaigns in mountainous areas has been brought to our attention many times recently – in Afghanistan. The Mujahideen used many mules to carry their supplies and equipment through the inhospitable mountains, but their own mules were relatively small, and many had been killed. The CIA then stepped in and the Rees brothers, probably the USA's biggest mule dealers, rounded up 7,000 large strong mules from Tennessee and Texas, which were flown out to Pakistan. It is said that because the guerillas were then better supplied, the Russians decided to pull out.

Howard Marshall, a professor at the University of Missouri, said, 'America never

Italian Army mule carrying the base-plate of a 120-mm mortar, 1965. (Photo: Major Ron Hill.)

lost a war in which they used mules.' The late Col. Keith Morgan-Jones, OBE, BVetMed, MRCVS, formerly officer commanding the RAVC Training Camp, and a great believer in mules based on his experience of them on army expeditions, wrote in 1983 that mules *would* be needed in the future. He felt strongly that helicopters had not replaced them, merely extended their range. Helicopters are expensive to buy, maintain and fly and are limited by weather and terrain.

Major Tylden expressed similar feelings:

> However complete and efficient mechanisation can be and however adequately modern aircraft can supply troops, in all sorts of terrain . . . the fact remains that over a large portion of the earth's surface the infantryman . . . must finish the job on his feet and must rely on the pack animal, which can creep or crawl almost anywhere a man can go and bring up ammunition, supplies and whatever else must be used in the fighting line.

The following was published in 1958, but is nevertheless just as true today:

BEHOLD THE MULE!

The Army, try as it will, can't get rid of its mules.

One by one mechanical marvels have appeared which narrow the ground on which the military mule, with his disproportionately dainty hoofs, has stood. The crawling tractor and the half-track speed bigger artillery faster.

But, the Army has found, none of these engines can pack a howitzer over mountain crags.

So the mule stays. He ought to – not alone for his sure-footedness, but for his character-moulding abilities. A couple of years ago, when the Turkish Army imported some 5,000 of these pertinacious hybrids, we warned that they were as likely to mould the characters of their masters as the other way around.

The mule possesses a willpower superior to most of his human associates and an intelligence the equal of many. He has sense of humour, boundless fortitude, a ferocious eye, a lethal hoof, and he can't be bullied. There are those in the Mississippi Valley who attribute many of the best qualities of Mark Twain, John J. Pershing, Omar Bradley and Harry Truman to boyhood proximity to mules.

Perhaps a few thousand ought to be attached to every training-camp to complement the influence of the drill sergeants and the 'boot drivers'.

(Horses and Mules and National Defense, Appendix 9)

Perhaps the last word should be given to Pat Carmichael:

In the years since these events [the campaigns in Southeast Asia in the latter part of World War II] I have often asked myself, is it right to use animals in war, submitting them to hardship and death? I am still uncertain of the answer because a plain 'No' is too facile a judgement. Until we have the wit to devise a machine which will do everything a mule can, silent and unseen in thick country or with assurance on the steep mountainside, he may continue to be indispensable. And when every man and woman is committed to a nation's fight for survival it is inevitable that all resources will be used. However, whatever the moral case may be, it is certain that everyone who served with these magnificent beasts gained immeasurably from the experience.

4 Scientific aspects

Almost since mules were originally bred they have been of great scientific interest for two reasons. First, it was soon realised that mules, like many other mammalian hybrids, are generally infertile, and scientists have attempted to explain this fact. Secondly, researchers in many other fields find mules invaluable as objects of study, largely because certain occurrences are more easily recognised in a hybrid with parents from two distict species.

The infertile mule

The male offspring of matings between two different species of mammal are believed to be always infertile, and so are most of the female offspring. For example, in the case of equines, the twenty-four species and sub-species can theoretically produce 276 crosses (discounting the additional factor of sexes, e.g. male donkey × female horse and female donkey × male horse). Of these crosses, only those listed below are generally believed to produce fertile offspring, and then only rarely:

Domestic Donkey	×	Nubian Wild Ass
Domestic Donkey	×	Somali Wild Ass
Domestic Donkey	×	Burchell's Zebra (rarely)
Domestic Donkey	×	Chapman's Zebra (rarely)
Domestic Donkey	×	Horse (rarely)
Nubian Wild Ass	×	Somali Wild Ass
Horse	×	Chapman's Zebra (rarely)
Horse	×	Mountain Zebra (questionable)
Horse	×	Przelwalski Horse

Despite the fact that in both male and female mules the internal and external sexual organs are quite normal, and both have the normal sexual urges, they are almost always infertile.

Research into infertility

The Romans were great mule breeders, and therefore had ample opportunity to realise that mules were generally infertile. They did, however, believe that mules could, very occasionally, give birth, although they believed such births to be portentous. Their phrase *cum mula peperit* (when a mule foals) is roughly equivalent to our 'once in a blue moon', and such an occurrence was said to accompany the birth of a great man, such as Julius Caesar, or was an omen that a city under siege would fall.

Aristotle had a 'seed and soil' theory of reproduction in which the male gave the 'seed' and the female provided the 'soil' in which it could grow. Although he correctly identified the 'seed' with semen, he was not aware of the existence of sperms, and of the production of eggs by females. Seeing the mule, he must have realised that its horse mother had contributed as much as its donkey father. The mule's lack of fertility was a problem which he had to consider, as both sexes showed the usual sexual behaviour, but of course he was not aware that the male's semen contained virtually no sperms and the female produced few and ineffective ova, but he did realise that female mules often only came into oestrus at irregular and sometimes infrequent intervals, and concluded that the infertility was entirely the female's fault, presumably believing the male mule could have produced a foal out of a horse or donkey.

In the seventeenth century, the Danish anatomist and physician Niels Stensen showed through anatomical investigation that the 'testes' of female mammals could be regarded as having a similar function to that of egg-laying animals. He even saw follicles in the ovaries of 'sterile' mules. His colleague, de Graaf, found this disturbing and suggested that sterility could be due to the 'unsuitability of the material of the eggs for conception' – a conclusion which may well be correct.

Scientific findings

Around the turn of the century, research by Ewart, Stephan, Ivanoff, Suchtev, Whitehead, Wodsedalek and others concentrated on studies of the testes of male mules, and it was discovered that few sperms were present, and those that were present were hardly motile.

Later, research was done on both males and females, particularly by Allen, Benirschke, Bielanski, Chandley, Short, Sullivan and Taylor. In the female mule's ovaries were found both egg follicles (in which eggs develop) and corpora lutea (the bodies formed after the follicle has ruptured to release the egg). The important question was whether the follicles actually contained eggs. Benirschke and Sullivan could not find a single egg in forty-seven mules, but Bielanski, studying three mules in 1963 and 1964, found one egg in one, three eggs in the second and none in the third. The surprising thing is not that more eggs were not found, but that any were found at all, as by rights they should never have developed.

The explanation for all this begins with the fact that the donkey has sixty-two chromosomes (thirty-one pairs), the horse sixty-four chromosomes (thirty-two pairs) and the mule and hinny each have sixty-three chromosomes – of which many pairs are unevenly matched. It is not just the number of chromosomes which is different in donkeys and horses, but their structure: they have developed slightly differently over evolutionary time. Taylor and Short found that in the early stages the reproductive cells inside a mule develop normally, but when they undergo the reduction division (meiosis) necessary to produce cells with half the parental chromosomes, they usually die. The donkey and horse chromosomes are almost completely unable to pair up, and unless this happens, meiosis cannot normally occur. Despite this, meiosis does occasionally occur and a few normal-looking egg cells result – although it is not known why!

A similar inability to form pairs and a breakdown in development explains the small number of sperms found in the males.

The studies of mules and hinnies concerning the reason for their sterility – and the occasional lack of sterility in the case of females – have been of assistance in understanding sterility in other mammals, including man.

Supposedly fertile mules

Since 1527 approximately sixty live births of foals to mules have been reported, in Europe, the USA, South America, North Africa and China.

Probably the best-known and best-documented of these until the 1980s was the case of Old Beck – and it is also the most difficult of the early cases to refute.

In 1920, having read in the *Farm and Ranch*, a Dallas weekly paper, of a mule having given birth to a live female offspring, named Kate, sired by a jack donkey, Professor W. D. Stangel of the Animal Husbandry Department of the A & M College of Texas visited the mule's owner, Mr Brantem. He arranged for the loan of the mule, Old Beck, and her foal to the college, and at the same time he secured affidavits from the owner and his neighbours with regard to Old Beck's parentage and the foal's birth.

The mule and her foal were studied closely, and certainly appeared to be quite normal mules. Put to a jack, the mule failed to conceive again, but in 1922 she was put to a stallion and produced a horse-like colt foal at the college, named Pat Murphy Junior. The foal was seen by members of the department within minutes of its birth, while it was still wet, and there was no possibility of any other mare having given birth to it. This colt, incidentally, proved to be fertile. Mated again, Old Beck aborted an abnormal foetus, and despite several attempts, never conceived again.

Because of the scepticism over Old Beck's fertility, blood tests were done on all three animals, Old Beck and Kate proving to be mules, Pat Murphy Junior being different, although no definite statement could be made about him. These tests were not sufficient to prove the case one way or the other, although on balance it does seem likely to be true.

Reactions to these reports

There have always been mixed reactions to reports of fertile mules. Such cases have been discounted by those who did not believe in them on one of the following counts:

1. The mother is not a mule, just looks like one.
(a) The supposed mule's mule-like appearance was often attributed to telegony, i.e. the 'mule's' mother had been mated with a donkey before being mated with the stallion which was the 'mule's' sire, and this caused her mule-like appearance, although she was really a horse. (Telegony is the term used for the theory that one mating can influence the offspring of a subsequent one. This matter was looked at scientifically at the end of the last century by Professor Cossar Ewart of Edinburgh in the famous Pennycuik Experiments – he thought the theory was untrue, but it seems likely that a belief in telegony still exists amongst some people.)
(b) The 'mule' is sometimes claimed to be a cross-bred horse of some sort, whose breeding has caused it to have a short mane, thin tail, long ears and a mule-like temperament. Certainly quite a number of horses do look very mule-like, as do some donkeys, and it can be quite difficult to tell them apart without close scrutiny.
(c) If the mother *were* a mule, the argument goes, the offspring by a horse should be three-quarters horse, one-quarter donkey, and if by a donkey, should be three-quarters donkey, one-quarter horse. In virtually every case the foal's appearance does not co-incide with this, a 'horse' being the result of mating with a horse, and a 'mule' being the result of mating with a donkey. Therefore the so-called mule must be a horse.

2.   The mother is a mule but the foal is not hers, just 'adopted'.

There are on record many cases of abnormal lactation amongst all levels of mammals, including humans. The maternal instinct is one of the most powerful in the animal world – even inter-species, in mules. William Tegetmeier reports:

> The case which I am about to put upon record is, I think, unprecedented, inasmuch as it is that of a sterile hybrid animal suckling another. The facts are as follows: an aged brown female mule . . . passed into the stables of Mr Cole of Church Street, Chelsea, who is well known as one who has employed mule labour with great advantage for many years. At the request of my friend Mr C. L. Sutherland, I accompanied him to the stables of Mr Cole, where we saw the mule in question and a young male donkey nearly a year old. This donkey foal had been bought and allowed to run about the stable yard. It had been noticed to follow the mule, and at night to go into her stall at the further end of the stable, where he was observed sucking the mule, whose udder, on examination, was found fully charged with milk . . . This case is interesting, inasmuch as it proves the secretion of milk can take place in a hybrid animal which is naturally sterile, and that it has no necessary connection with the maternal relations. (*The Field*, 17 April 1880)

Some people believe that a mule cannot give birth yet believe that it can conceive. Betsy Hutchins of the American Donkey and Mule Society states a belief that mules can carry foals but always abort, and an old Hindu belief is that mules who get pregnant must always die before they are ready to give birth.

3.   There are many places where large numbers of mules are run with both horse and donkey stallions, e.g. in Poitou, where many thousands of mules are bred annually, and yet none of the mules gives birth.

4.   The owner of a mule which was proved to be fertile would have a considerable amount to gain both financially and in status, which is a good enough reason for attempts to be made to pass off a horse or donkey as a mule, or a foal as a mule's own, either in good faith or in a deliberate attempt at fraud.

On the other hand, few of the reported cases have actually been disproved, and some of them are extremely well documented with sworn affidavits from army officers, veterinary surgeons and so on, whom we might expect to believe, particularly in the case of Old Beck. The announcement of the existence of a fertile mule would also

	MALE HORSE	MALE DONKEY
FEMALE HORSE	HORSE	MULE
FEMALE DONKEY	HINNY	DONKEY
FEMALE MULE	HORSE	MULE
FEMALE HINNY	HINNY	DONKEY

(PARENT / PARENT)

Crosses between horse, donkey, mule and hinny.

draw many interested people, including many experts, and it would presumably be difficult to fool all of them.

One important fact to be noted from the reported cases is the consistency in the appearance of the offspring: a foal out of a mule by a horse is horse-like, and by a donkey is mule-like. A foal out of a hinny by a horse is hinny-like and by a donkey is donkey-like. Those who did not believe that mules can occasionally be fertile have used this fact as proof that the so-called mules were actually horses, and the so-called hinnies were actually donkeys, but this seems rather surprising. Unless every owner of a supposedly fertile mule knew the details of earlier cases (which was impossible until fairly recent times) it is difficult to believe that horse-owners would all pass them off as mules, but donkey-owners pass them off as hinnies. To many people, the consistency seemed instead to point to the likelihood that these reports were true.

Following a debate on this subject in the British Mule Society's journal in 1980, Dr Ann Chandley, a research scientist with the Medical Research Council's Clinical and Population Cytogenetics Unit, who had done previous work on infertility in the mule, came up with a theory which might explain the occasional fertile mules.

> In the 1950s Dr Donald Michie had discovered a phenomenon which allows the segregation of whole maternal and paternal chromosome sets to opposite poles during egg or sperm formation in inter-specific hybrids of the mouse and several other species.

If similar 'affinity' were to operate in the mule or hinny, Dr Chandley suggested,

> it would make possible the segregation of whole horse or donkey chromosome sets into the gametes, and chromosomally-balanced eggs and spermatozoa could thus be formed. Theoretically this is a possibility, although there is no direct evidence yet to support the idea. However, from the types of progeny produced by the allegedly fertile she-mules or hinnies, only those eggs containing maternal sets of chromosomes appear to produce viable pregnancies. This could mean either that eggs containing paternal chromosome sets are eliminated or that the foetuses derived from them are slipped.

The breakthrough

Later that year, writing in the same journal, Dr Chandley described her theory of affinity, and said that as the tests were now available to prove definitely whether or not a reported case of a fertile mule was genuine, she hoped that a fertile mule would turn up soon.

She did not really expect it to happen, but her wish was granted very shortly. She – and many others – were amazed and delighted to receive a translation of a newspaper cutting from Yin County, Honan Province, China:

> The production of a foal by a female mule is something which surpasses all expectation. Shortly after 11 pm on 4th March [1981] a female mule gave birth to a light grey coloured female mule foal in the number two production team of the Tielu production brigade in Yin County, Honan Province. This mule foal is 85 cm high, 48 cm long, 68.5 cm round the chest, 27 kilos in weight, of strong physique, lively and attractive and people from hundreds of li away have come in droves to look at it.
>
> From time immemorial people have believed that mules could not produce a further generation. Comrades who have done research on animal husbandry believe that the reasons why mules cannot reproduce are as follows: firstly, a mule ? combines distant hybridisation (?), and the reproductive organs are not sufficiently developed for reproduction; secondly, the temperature of the vagina and uterus of the mule are too high, and thus it cannot conceive. This mule was 7½ years old this year, of long build, well-covered, sweet-natured, dark chestnut in colour, and until she dropped her foal the stockmen and assistants did not have the slightest inkling that she had been on heat and become pregnant. After the event, commune officials made it known that she had become pregnant after a natural mating with a male donkey in the same brigade. The fact that this mule has produced a foal will be very valuable in the research and investigations into the reproduction of mules.

Shortly afterwards, Dr Rong Ruizhang, a Chinese geneticist, wrote to Dr Chandley about this case. The Institute of Genetics, Academia Sinica, Beijing, where Dr Rong worked, had bought the mule and her foal, and had done studies of them. He sent photographs and the results of tests on the chromosomes of the mule and her offspring. Dr Chandley sent me one of the photographs of the foal, which had been named 'Dragon Foal', and asked me what it looked like. My husband, John, and I both studied it independently, and each of us rather sheepishly announced that parts of it looked like a mule, but other parts of it, particularly the tail

Dragon Foal (donkey × mule), aged five, with Dr Rong in Beijing. (Photo: Dr Ann Chandley.)

and legs, looked more like a donkey. Of course, this was impossible – it had never been heard of for the offspring of a hybrid to look like a cross between its hybrid dam and its pure sire. We were amazed – and rather gratified – to discover that the studies of the foal's chromosomes had shown similar results!

The father being a donkey, according to the affinity theory the offspring should be a mule, but from the photographs and results, it was apparent that it was not. Dr Rong suggested, and the photographs appeared to support him, that it was half donkey and half mule – the first time that such an occurrence had been reported. Unfortunately, the test results were not of very good quality, and could not be used as definite proof of an authentic case, so Dr Chandley arranged for further chromosome samples to be taken, and the material to be sent to her laboratory where more accurate results could be obtained.

Study of this material left her in no doubt that the mother of the foal was a genuine mule. Blood tests then had to be taken to establish beyond doubt that she was the mother of the foal. Sadly, the mule died before these could be completed, but as three witnesses, including a vet, were present at the birth, there was little doubt of this.

Studies of the foal's chromosomes confirmed what the photographs suggested. Her chromosome count was sixty-two (not the sixty-three chromosomes of a mule, as expected), with certain of the chromosomes being intermediate between mule and donkey. In sex chromosome constitution she was pure donkey, providing evidence that her sire was a jack donkey, as had been stated. The mule had also passed on several clearly identifiable donkey chromosomes. Horse chromosomes that have no equivalent in the donkey could also be identified, showing that she was a donkey/horse hybrid. A simple bio-chemical test on her blood also showed her to be a hybrid and not simply a donkey. She did not, however, have a straightforward one to one ratio of horse/donkey chromosomes, as in the mule and hinny, and thus appeared to be a novel kind of hybrid never before encountered. Despite this very strange chromosomal make-up, she was strong and sound, whereas it might have been supposed that an animal with such a strange mixture of chromosomes would not be viable.

In 1986 Dr Chandley and a colleague flew to Beijing to do more tests on Dragon Foal and a hinny which had recently been reported to have given birth. The latter turned out, on investigation, to be genuinely a fertile hinny and her foal had, like Dragon Foal, a fascinating mixture of horse and donkey chromosomes, not at all what would have been expected. Her father had been a donkey, so in theory she should have turned out donkey-like, but her chromosome count should then have been sixty-two, whereas it was sixty-three, some horse, some donkey, in a strange mixture.

Dr Rong said he had heard of several other fertile mules and hinnies in China, but was not very optimistic about the chances of obtaining blood samples on which to perform chromosome investigations.

In the meantime, on 6 July 1984, a mule gave birth in America. Krause was bred by

The mule Krause (*back left*) with her foals by a donkey: Blue Moon (*right*) and White Lightning (*front*). (Photo: Betsy Hutchins.)

Bill and Oneta Silvester of Champion, Nebraska, out of a Welsh pony mare by Chester, a jack donkey. The Silvesters had no idea Krause was in foal until they went out one morning to see a newborn foal running behind her. Their local vet examined Krause and said there was no doubt at all that she had given birth. She contacted Betsy Hutchins of the American Donkey and Mule Society, who put her in touch with Dr Kurt Benirschke of the Centre for the Reproduction of Endangered Species at San Diego Zoo, who had previously done research into the mule's infertility. Tests began immediately, blood samples being taken of the foal (christened Blue Moon, because of the Roman saying, *cum mula peperit*), Krause and Chester, who was the foal's father as well as his grandfather. The tests proved that Krause and Chester were indeed the parents, and also that Krause was indeed a mule. Chromosomal analysis showed that, in line with the affinity theory, Blue Moon was a pure mule.

The Silvesters attempted to get Krause in foal again, so that this time the experts could keep an eye on her throughout her pregnancy. Success eluded them for a while, but on 11 November 1987 Krause gave birth for a second time, the sire again being Chester. This foal, another male, was named White Lightning, because lightning never strikes twice in the same place! The scientists again converged on Champion, tests were carried out, and again it was proved that Krause, the mule, had given birth to a mule foal. Since then she has been served again, this time by a horse stallion.

News then came that a mule had foaled in Brazil and was in foal again, and was being studied by Dr Marc Henry, a Belgian vet working in Brazil. In 1986, while

The Brazilian mule's first foal, sired by a horse, aged one year in 1987. (The second foal was almost identical.) (Photo: Marc Henry and Eduardo Gastal.)

doing research into reproduction of horses and donkeys, he had been told of a fertile mule and went to investigate. The mule had been bought as a foal and run with two horse stallions, and at the age of 3½, on 15 November 1986, she had been found with a colt foal. Chromosomal analysis showed her to be a mule, one of the stallions to be the foal's father, and the foal to be pure horse, in line with the affinity theory. The mule was served again by the same stallion on 21 December 1986, and after 348 days she foaled again, on 4 December 1987, again producing a colt foal. Tests again proved the case to be genuine – the mule was the colt's mother, and he was a horse. The mare was served again on 27 February 1988, but this time by artificial insemination using donkey semen. In February 1989 she duly foaled, bringing a colt foal which appears to be pure mule, as expected, although at the time of going to press successful tests on its chromosomes have yet to be done, to confirm or

Brazilian mule and her third foal, product of a donkey father, 1989. (Photo: Marc Henry and Eduardo Gastal.)

One of the foals produced by a fertile hinny in China. (Photo: Prof. Zong.)

otherwise that this is the case. The mule has been served again by a horse, and is pregnant yet again!

As the first two foals are pure horses they could well be fertile, as Old Beck's horse foal was said to be, and it will be interesting to discover whether this is indeed the case.

In 1988 Dr Ann Chandley sent me twelve photographs on which she wanted an opinion: did they appear to be what they were claimed to be, and to what extent did they look like horse, donkey, mule or hinny? Afterwards she told me the whole story. Professor Zong Enze at the Research Institute of Animal Science, Lanzhou in Gansu Province of China, had written a paper entitled 'The variety of sterility and gradual progression to fertility in hybrids of the horse and donkey', and Dr Chandley had been asked to look it over. Professor Zong and his colleagues had been investigating various features of a large number of mules and hinnies since the mid-1950s, and this was the first that the West had heard about their work.

The twelve animals photographed were the offspring of fertile mules or hinnies, ten by jack donkeys and two by horse stallions. Chromosome investigations were carried out on eight of these offspring, but the results given were somewhat inadequate. In her article in the British Mule Society journal describing this, Dr Chandley said:

> The statement I made in an Editorial to the *Journal of the Royal Society of Medicine* earlier this year that 'there may be more fertile mules than has ever previously been supposed' seems certainly turning out to be true. Up until only three years ago the dogma decreed that these hybrids were sterile and the scientific world would have none of it that fertility could exist. Now we know better.

Other scientific aspects

Professor Roger Short, writing in the *Journal of Reproductive Fertility* in 1975, detailed the contribution of the mule to scientific thought. Some of the points he made are listed here, other than the early studies of mule fertility which have already been mentioned.

The female mule has provided a valuable clue about the factors that determine the length of the oestrous cycle. A mule's oestrous cycle can be of normal length (twenty-two days) or it can be as long as 900 days. If follicular development and ovulation were determined entirely by pituitary gonadotrophic activity, one would expect the severely depleted stock of oocytes in the mule's ovary to be rapidly exhausted in the early years of life as a result of the combined effects of atresia and ovulation. Thus one would have expected mules to have regular oestrous cycles for a brief period after puberty, before lapsing into permanent anoestrus. This is obviously not the case.

The situation in the mule can best be explained by postulating that there is a hierarchy of follicles in the ovary, spontaneously progressing from a stage in which they are completely refractory to gonadotrophic stimulation, through various degrees of increasing sensitivity, until ultimately they are capable of secreting sufficient oestrogen to induce ovulation. Thus when the stock of follicles is severely depleted, long periods of time may elapse between the maturation of successive follicles to the gonadotrophin-sensitive stage, so that the cycles become very prolonged.

Such a hierarchy of gonadotrophin sensitivity is very reminiscent of the 'production line' hypothesis of oocyte maturation advanced by Henderson and Edwards, and it would explain the progressive increase in length of the human menstrual cycle as oocyte stocks become depleted with the approach of the menopause. The mule has therefore shown that when the number of oocytes in the ovary becomes a limiting factor, the ovary itself is probably the time-clock that determines the length of the oestrous or menstrual cycle.

The mule has also contributed to our understanding of early pregnancy in the horse and donkey. In these species, foetal cells from the chorionic girdle invade the endometrium to form the endometrial cups which subsequently secrete large amounts of gonadotrophin into the maternal circulation during the first third of a pregnancy. At the same time they begin to elicit a maternal immune response, so that they are eventually sloughed from the uterus in response to a classical host-against-graft rejection mechanism. The production of this placental gonadotrophin assumed new significance when it was discovered that if a mare was carrying a mule foetus, no gonadotrophin was produced. A more detailed investigation showed that mares carrying mules did indeed produce very little placental gonadotrophin, whereas large amounts were produced by donkeys carrying hinnies.

The mule and the hinny have also helped to shed some new light on the mechanism of action of the sex chromosomes. Lyon proposed that only one of the two X-chromosomes was active in the somatic cells of female mammals; the inactivation process was thought to be a random event that took place early in embryonic life. But attractive though this hypothesis was, it was difficult to test. Then it was realised that the female mule and hinny provided the ideal test situation. The X-chromosomes of the horse and donkey are morphologically distinct from one another, and carry a species-specific glucose-6-phosphate dehydrogenase locus. Thus it is possible to have both a morphological and biochemical marker of the paternally and maternally derived X-chromosomes in the cells of the hybrid. In this way it was possible to confirm that in any given cell only one of the two X-chromosomes was functional, and that this property was transmitted to all daughter cells. But in contrast to random inactivation, it seemed that there was a preferential inactivation of the donkey X-chromosome in both the mule and hinny; there was also evidence of further cell selection in culture. Thus the female mule and hinny are genetically slightly more horse- than donkey-like.

The mule has become living proof of the genetic doctrine of hybrid vigour, and in addition it has provided remarkable confirmatory evidence in support of Haldane's

Law. Haldane proposed that, in inter-specific hybrids, the heterogametic sex (i.e. the one with unlike sex chromosomes, in this case the male) was the more likely to be either absent, rare or sterile. There are certainly many anecdotal accounts of fertile female mules and none of fertile males, and it is easier to imagine a female mule very occasionally producing a single fertile egg than a male mule producing sufficient normal spermatozoa for a fertile mating. Haldane's Law also seems to be borne out by an analysis of the sex ratio of mules at birth, an analysis showing that there were only 44 per cent of males, which departs significantly from the normal horse sex ratio of 52.5 per cent males.

Embryo transfer

Embryo transfer is gradually becoming commercially viable in all types of domestic animal, although it is very rarely used in equines. In the late 1970s Dr W. R. 'Twink'

Mule with her donkey 'foal' produced by embryo transfer. (Photo: Dr W. R. Allen.)

82

Allen had transplanted horse embryos into donkey surrogate mothers, and these usually developed quite normally, but of twenty-two donkey embryos transplanted into a horse's uterus, twenty-one aborted. It was decided to find out whether a female mule, which carries both horse and donkey genes, would provide a suitable uterine environment for the development of either a horse or donkey. In other words, a mule would act as a neutral vehicle for studying what can go right and wrong in equine pregnancies. Information could be gained about the significance of immunological responses associated with equine species. Also, by splitting an embryo to create identical twins, and implanting one in a horse and one in a mule, the non-genetic effects on development could be studied. In a study carried out with Professor Doug Antzac at Cornell University, five mules were made pregnant by the implantation of fertilised eggs, one aborting spontaneously and one being surgically interrupted for examination of the placenta in the mule's uterus, the remaining three giving birth during the summer of 1984.

Useful information was gained about the limit of the difference in size between donor parents and recipients. Goblet, a horse and the first foal to be born, had long legs in comparison to his surrogate mother (who was much smaller than the Thoroughbred donor parents) but average for a Thoroughbred. He was born with a cleft palate (believed to be unrelated to the embryo transplantation) and this was corrected surgically, with great success. The second horse foal and a donkey foal were born shortly afterwards, both perfect, and all three are doing very well.

5 Mule ownership

In many ways mule ownership is similar to that of horses and donkeys, and this chapter therefore concentrates on ways in which it differs.

Having decided that a mule is wanted in preference to a horse or donkey, the first step is to decide what type of mule he should be. As mules can be bred to any size, shape and weight, thought must be given to the future use of the mule. For example, someone mainly interested in driving may choose a small animal, which will cost less to feed and house than a larger one, and the cart and harness for it may be a little cheaper. In this case, a mule out of a native pony by an ordinary British jack donkey may well be ideal. Such a mule would also be ideal for a child, teenager or small adult to ride.

If the mule will be expected to cover long distances, or do hard work, one bred from bigger, heavier parents should be considered: a Welsh cob, Ardennes or similar mare with plenty of bone, mated with a Poitou or part-bred Poitou jack, such as are now available at stud in Britain. For a show jumper, eventer or similar, or for an elegant driving turnout, a finer-boned mare could be chosen, perhaps a part-Thoroughbred, put to either a Poitou or a Spanish jack.

The temperament of the future mule is also something to be considered. Should it be a lively, high-spirited animal, or one which is quiet and affectionate? The choice of parents will have a good deal to do with this.

Buying

If a suitable mare is not available, or if the mule is required urgently, buying is the only answer. Having decided on the type of mule needed according to the use to which he will be put, another point to consider is the sex. This is very much a matter of personal preference, as with horses or donkeys, but mares do seem easier to handle, and stallions must be gelded, as they start to become very high-spirited and possibly dangerous, and either fight with other males or chase and serve mares.

Age is another consideration. If there is no great hurry to use him immediately, it is best to buy a foal. This has the disadvantage that it is not possible to know exactly what the finished product will be like (although as with horses, seeing the parents will help), but it has the big advantage that there has been very little time for the mule to be wrongly treated, to have learned to dislike or distrust humans or to have developed any bad habits. Also, his exact age will be known, and there will be no doubt that he is well-reared and properly handled.

A slightly older but still unhandled mule can be a good buy and not too difficult to find, as many mules, being 'accidents', are unwanted and more or less ignored by their owners. Getting to know them can be more difficult when they are older – and bigger and stronger – but there is the advantage that they have outgrown (one hopes) the silly, babyish pretending-to-be-frightened ways many mules have in their first months of life. The older the mule, the more chance that he will have developed bad habits, and an older mule should preferably be well broken.

Temperament is of vital importance, and it should be possible to get some idea of this even in a few minutes. If the mule is young and unbroken, he can be expected to be nervous; his trust can be won with time and patience. A broken mule, however, should not kick or bite – or be difficult to catch, hard to saddle up, unwilling to stand still or to have any part of his anatomy handled.

Buying a horse or pony is relatively easy. It is possible to find one by looking in newspapers and magazines, asking friends, perhaps going to sales, and if an animal is unsuitable it can be turned down and the search continued. With mules, however, very few come on the market, and once the decision has been made to buy a mule, it will be hard to wait for months before a purchase is completed! It is therefore very tempting to buy the first passable mule which comes along, regardless of whether he is really suitable. I know, I've done it!

It is a mistake to go to look at a mule thinking that he sounds ideal and that waiting until another turns up would be unbearable. Be prepared to come away without him. Remember all the tricks people can get up to when selling any animal; arrive early and be wary if the animal is already tacked or harnessed up. It is much better to see him caught up in the field and the tack/harness put on him – or at least a halter or head collar if he is not said to be broken. If he *is* said to be broken, he must be tried out. Accept no excuses – *do not be afraid of seeming rude!* If the mule is genuine the owner will be pleased to show off what he can do, and if he won't, don't buy. A well-broken mule is a great joy, but a badly broken, mishandled animal can be a real problem, so great care should be taken. The ideal is to have him on a week or two week trial. Check all the usual signs of good health, and find out whether he has any dislikes, such as traffic, fertiliser bags or men in flat caps.

Good signs are if the mule comes up to people and is interested in them, is happy to be handled by strangers, will stand quietly without being tied up, helps you to put the headcollar/bridle/collar on. Do not be fooled by hard-luck stories about what will happen to the poor little mule if he is not sold to a kind home at once. If he cannot be shown to do what he is said to do, but you still decide that you want him, insist on the price being brought down drastically; be hard hearted. Do not appear too enthusiastic, because it is very easy for the price to go up if the seller sees how keen you are to buy. Prices for small, unbroken mules are relatively low, but for a big, well-broken animal you may well have to pay more than for a similar horse, as at the moment they are few and far between.

Breeding

The vast majority of mules in Britain today are accidents. A jack donkey and a horse or pony mare (or vice versa) are kept in a field together and a surprised – but not always delighted – owner finds that his mare has produced a long-eared foal. Quite often the mule foals are unwanted, unappreciated and disposed of at an early age. They may also be of poor quality, which is even more reason for them being unwanted.

When breeding a mule, the best quality parents must be chosen. In the past, many people believed that the contribution of the female to the offspring was negligible, and therefore while the sires were carefully chosen, poor quality mares were believed to be quite acceptable as dams. Gradually breeders realised the error of their ways and, for example, the famous Kentucky mule breeders always chose the best quality cart-horse mares, producing mules of consistently high quality. It should be borne in mind, however, that the appearance of the potential parents is somewhat less important than the quality of their progeny. Elegant, well-conformed parents will not necessarily produce good mules, and poor-looking parents will not necessarily produce poor mules. To give one example, the heavy-boned, long-haired donkeys of Poitou and the 'common' cart-horse mares to which they are put are thought by many people (not me!) to be extremely ugly, but the mules they produce are strong, well-conformed, high quality and have been in great demand for a thousand years. When choosing parents, therefore, it is most helpful if some of their earlier mule progeny can be seen.

Before going into detail about parents, a word about the size of progeny may be useful. The size of both parents is important in determining the size of their offspring, but the mare's size is more important: the bigger the mare the bigger her womb and therefore the bigger the foal she can carry. Mules, having hybrid vigour, are said to be able to grow larger than either parent, and certainly if the parents are of similar

86

Kit, product of a jack donkey and a pony mare, at one week old.

size, this seems to be true, although if one is much taller than the other, one cannot expect the foal to be taller than the taller of its parents. However, mules do tend to grow bigger than one might predict for a horse foal with parents of similar size. For example, my 13.2 hh mare was served by my 10 hh donkey (with difficulty!) and the resulting mule, Kit, is around 12.3 hh and probably has another inch or so to grow. The same jack donkey served a 36-inch miniature Shetland, and her foal, Bryony, is bigger than her father. Hinnies are said not to have hybrid vigour, and with the same sized parents should be slightly smaller than a mule. They are *said* to be always smaller than mules, but this is probably because they are usually bred out of a donkey mare smaller than the horse stallion which served her.

(*Left*)
Bryony, product of a jack donkey and a miniature Shetland mare, one day old.

(*Opposite page*)
Jubilee, by a Poitou jack, with her Thoroughbred mother, Girl Talk. (Photo: Robert Way.)

The size of the foal will, of course, be affected to a small extent by the environment in which it is reared – its health, the climate and principally the way it is fed.

Little is known about the amount of bone one can expect a mule to inherit from its parents. To be on the safe side I would try to choose both parents with the amount of bone I wanted from the mule foal, but my feeling is that the amount of bone the mare has is more important. For example, large-boned Poitou donkeys crossed with large-boned Poitou mares produce large-boned mules, while Eclair, a pure Poitou donkey put on to Girl Talk, Robert Way's Thoroughbred mare, produced Jubilee, who is almost pure Thoroughbred in appearance including her fine bone. Kit has inherited her mother's heavy bone, not her father's light bone.

It is not really possible to predict colour, although it seems that if the mare is grey

or roan, there is a good chance that the mule will be roan, and roans are the most common colours for hinnies. In Britain the most common colour for mules is dark bay, although in other countries other colours are dominant. It is not really known why this should be, although no doubt future research will throw some light on the matter.

Choosing the jack

Many people wanting to breed a mule will be content to use whatever jack is easily available to them, and this will, in Great Britain, usually be a typical British donkey of 11 hh or less, with fine bones, narrow chest, long weak back and weak joints. (The

Black Bart, a US National Champion American Mammoth Jack owned by Don and Irma Mode. (Photo: Betsy Hutchins.)

Donkey Breed Society may perhaps be a little upset by this description, but it is all relative – relative to the ideal mule-breeding donkey!) An enthusiastic donkey, given help, can serve a mare of three hands or more taller than himself, and even a small donkey can therefore produce a useful-sized mule. However, for a mule suitable for most riding activities, something of 14 hh upwards is generally required, and here a big donkey is necessary.

To many people the ideal is an American Mammoth Jack whose background was

90

described in Chapter 2. The minimum height is 14 hh for jacks and 13.2 hh for jennies, larger jacks up to 15.2 hh being preferred but fairly uncommon. These jacks produce, out of good mares, mules of good quality, size and temperament. Unfortunately there are none in Britain at present, and to buy one in the USA would be expensive – a good weanling would cost around £1,000 apart from transport and various administration costs.

The most highly prized breed of mule-breeding donkey in Europe has, for about 1,000 years, been the Poitou donkey, from the region of Poitou in France. Little is known about its origins, but it is quite unlike any other breed of donkey, having an enormous amount of bone, large long head, long straight back, often ewe-necked and – most surprising – a long, silky, tangled coat. It is usually bay, sometimes yellowish, and approximately 14–15 hh in height. The jacks were always only bred

Poitou jack donkey, with a typical shaggy coat, in a French farmyard. (Photo: Michael Northen by courtesy of the International Donkey Protection Trust.)

for mule breeding, not for work, although the jennies, which were considered of little value, were sometimes used for work.

To digress for a moment, the Poitou area was in the past very well organised, with the donkeys bred in certain areas, and in other areas the *mulassier* breed of horses, of which the mares were bred specially for mule production, being 15.1–16.1 hh, very heavy and good-natured. The mules resulting from this cross were as tall as their dams: 15.1–16.1 hh, and approximately halfway in weight between sire and dam. Unfortunately, the advance of mechanisation led to a reduced demand for mules, particularly from 1950 onwards, and consequently for the jacks and mares required to produce them. At the end of the nineteenth century there were well over 200,000 mules in France, and a proved mule-getting jack was worth £200–£320 or more, the industry still being very important to the area. In 1949 there were only 218 jacks (and 340 jennies) in Poitou, and by 1977 there were only twelve jacks (and thirteen jennies). Annual registrations in the donkey section of the Mule-Breeding Studbook of Poitou for the same period fell from 125 (93 males and 32 females) to only seven (three males and four females). Corresponding registrations in the horse section of the Studbook were 13 colts and 32 fillies in 1948 and 7 colts and 21 fillies in 1976. There had for a long time been a problem of fertility, and, presumably as a result of inbreeding, this worsened: in 1976 73 per cent of recorded services did not produce a live birth.

The sad state of the breed attracted attention in the 1970s, and the French government stepped in to do something about it – as well as various zoos, organisations and individuals in other countries. One such is the International Donkey Protection Trust, based in Devon, which is working with the French authorities, breeders and SABAUD (the Association to Safeguard the Poitou) to help the breed survive. It is setting up a blood-typing programme, and is also hoping that a process can be set up whereby semen can be frozen and stored. Breeding and management methods have always been very traditional and idiosyncratic (such as preventing the donkey foals from drinking their mother's colostrum, which is usually considered by other people to be essential in giving the foal protection from future infection), so advice and assistance has been given to the very few remaining breeders. In addition, a back-up programme has been set up to put 13.1–13.3 hh good quality Portuguese jenny donkeys to Poitou jacks, keeping the jenny foals and, in due course, putting them back to a different Poitou jack, over several generations producing Poitous which are almost purebred and indistinguishable from the actual purebred. The half-bred colt foals are sold off at around £500, and some of these are

A fine pair of Poitou mules in the 1930s. (Photo: Lydia Sacki.)

finding their way to England, as well as some of the purebred Poitou jacks and jennies, but the latter are very difficult to buy and therefore very expensive. A California veterinary surgeon, Sharon Vanderlip, has also imported several pure Poitou foals to the United States, and is breeding with them in order to help preserve the breed.

To return to the discussion on types of mule-breeding jack, there are also good, big, but less heavy donkeys, suitable for mule breeding in Spain, Portugal, Italy and Greece (and of course many other countries further from Britain), but again the cost of purchase and transport and administration is high – perhaps too high at present for most people.

It is certain that with more jacks being imported and the existing big jacks in Britain being put to biggish jennies, there will soon be a good choice of jacks here.

Assuming that one has a choice of jack, one should choose an animal which is

Marwell Zoo's Poitou × Portuguese jack, Uranus. (Marwell Zoo.)

strongly built with a good loin and rump (usually weak in donkeys); a fairly level croup; good clean, strong head with straight profile and long alert ears; eyes large, open, kind and lively; long, straight neck, not concave or very short; sloping shoulders (these are usually straight in donkeys); good withers (usually donkeys have none); good action with a long stride; belly and flanks well let down and strongly ribbed, broad chest (donkeys are usually narrow); legs straight, strong and properly set with good bone; feet large and open. If possible his offspring should be inspected. If the jack is to be bought rather than just used, he should be guaranteed to serve mares, as many jacks do not do this willingly!

It is perhaps as well here to consider some alternatives to using a jack donkey. Artificial insemination is useful if, for example, the only jack available is more than three hands smaller than the mare to be used, and he cannot reach her, or if the jack or mare object to the coupling. Fresh semen can be used successfully and with few problems. If there is no jack donkey convenient, the next best thing, rather than travelling the mare enormous distances, might be to use chilled semen from the chosen jack. Used within 24–36 hours this is nearly as successful as fresh semen. It is even possible now to use frozen semen from an American Mammoth Jack, as the organisation and facilities for doing this are all available. The cost in 1989 was approximately $130 per straw 'delivered to the mare's backside' – this is in addition to the cost of having her inseminated, which would need to be done by an expert, and could therefore be fairly expensive. The big problem with frozen semen is that, however much care is taken over choice of jack, freezing procedures and so on, the odds of the mare conceiving are low. It may be necessary to use several straws before the mare conceives, which would be expensive and time-consuming. It is, however, bound to be cheaper than importing an American Mammoth Jack or a mule sired by one. The technology also exists for transferring a mule or donkey embryo into a much smaller animal such as a rabbit, which is far cheaper to transport, and then transferring back into an equine surrogate mother.

Choosing the mare

Many people already own a mare and decide to breed a mule from her, but if setting out to choose a mare, the choice is both much easier than choosing a jack – because there are so many good mares from which to choose; and harder – because we are rather spoilt for choice.

The most important consideration, I feel, is temperament. She should be quiet and kind, alert and intelligent, not sluggish, stupid or stubborn. Native ponies and cobs tend to make good dams of mules, but when choosing a horse, pure Thoroughbreds, Hackneys, trotters and similar highly-strung animals should be avoided.

Given the limited choice of jack donkey, the right mare should be chosen to produce the size, weight and shape of mule required. An old saying goes that a good brood mare should have 'a head like my lady's maid but a bottom like the cook's'. Good conformation for a brood mare is much the same as for one put to a stallion, so we will not go into it here except to say that the faults in conformation of the donkey should be compensated for in the mare. Most commonly she needs to have prominent withers, very sloping shoulders, strong legs (very important) with plenty of bone and good feet, short strong back, good tail set high up (not goose-rumped), broad chest, deep and well rounded body and strong quarters.

Serving the mare

When mating equines, the main decision to be made is whether the male should serve the female in a yard under strict control, or running with her in the pasture. My own preference is for the latter, if the stallion or jack is of suitable temperament, despite the possible problems caused by probably not knowing exactly when the mare was served. With mule breeding there is an extra problem, in that not all jacks are willing to serve mares.

Traditionally in mule-breeding areas, precautions were taken to prevent this problem arising. Young jacks were taken off their donkey mothers before weaning and put to suckle on a horse mare. At weaning the jacks were turned away with horse colts, to learn to cope with the rough and tumble of 'horse play', and were not allowed to see any donkeys. They were fed really well, with plenty of corn to make them very fit and active.

When, at two to three years of age, a jack is old enough to serve his first mare (never a jenny donkey – that comes much later, if at all), he is tried for several short periods with a small, quiet, experienced mare who will stand for him without kicking. Sight and smell are apparently the strongest sexual stimulants, so traditionally the mare's mane was cut short to look like a donkey's, as the mane is the object he will see most of during mating. This ploy goes back to Roman times. Smearing the mare's vulva with the vaginal secretions of a donkey was also said to increase the donkey's interest in serving her. Warm weather makes some donkeys more willing to serve mares, presumably because they are, historically, animals of warm climates. If the mare is not sufficiently quiet she should be hobbled to prevent her kicking him and putting him off. If the mare is too big, she should be made to stand in a pit. (Having said all this, when my small jack donkey was attempting – for many months – to serve the bigger mare, she kicked him so hard I feared she had broken one of his ribs, but he was never deterred, and by standing on a steep hillside, finally managed to serve her.)

If the jack seemed unwilling to do his duty, the traditional Poitou trick was to mesmerise him. The stablemen joined hands and circled round him singing the aphrodisiacal 'la-la-la' chorus, a method known as 'la lalandage'! A less picturesque method is to 'tease' him with an in-season jenny donkey and, just as he is about to serve her, substitute the mare.

Occasionally a mare will not be willing to be served by a donkey, and for what it is worth I quote a method used by an old Kansas mule breeder. He turned a two-year-old uncastrated mule stallion out with the mare. It tended to be rather amorous, and kept trying to serve the mare, however often she kicked him. Thus she was accustomed to seeing long ears over her back, and was not worried when the jack donkey was turned out with her.

Incidentally, it has been found that, not infrequently, mares who were apparently infertile have conceived for the first time when served by a jack donkey. The Hungarian State Studs use this method, and the high-quality mules which result are much prized for harness work. My jack donkey sired two mules out of a Shetland mare who had never produced a pony foal, but following the two mules she then produced her first pony foal.

The gestation period for mules is approximately eleven and a half months, halfway between that for horses and for donkeys, although as with horses and donkeys, approximately is the operative word.

Management

The management of mules is very similar to that of horses and donkeys, and there are many excellent books on the subject, so here again I shall restrict myself to discussing the subject very briefly with particular reference to mules.

In the field

The acreage required will of course vary depending on the size of the mule (although for its size a mule generally needs less food than a horse); the quality of the grazing (a mule, like many native ponies, can thrive on rough grazing which would be inadequate for a horse); whether or not alternative grazing is available for part of the year to give the mule's field a rest; and possibly other factors.

The field should have at least some flat ground, should be free of holes, obstructions or other dangers, and should be well drained and not too low-lying as both the mule's feet and the field will suffer if it is wet for long periods.

The grass should ideally include a variety of other plants, but beware of poisonous plants such as ragwort (mules will not normally eat these, but will eat ragwort when it is dead and no longer has its bitter warning taste). It must be remembered, also, that mules are excellent jumpers, so checks should be made in neighbouring land, such as gardens, for poisonous plants, including rhubarb, laburnum and yew. Beware, also, grass which is too rich, particularly in spring, when the mule could get laminitis (although mules are far less prone to this than horses, partly because they stop eating when they have had enough instead of gorging themselves) and should be kept off it for part of the day if there is a lot of grass. The field should be rested periodically to prevent it becoming horse- (sorry, mule-) sick. If the grass has just been mown, the mule should be kept off it for a week or so to allow the young shoots to grow, and for three weeks if the field has been fertilised. If the acreage is big enough, the ground should be divided into several smaller areas in order to rest each area in turn. If not, it should if possible be rested for short periods by finding alternative grazing, or by keeping the mule inside if there is no other way. It is advisable to pick up the mule's droppings every day if the acreage is very small. Worming will be covered below, but on a small acreage a mule should be wormed regularly.

A constant supply of fresh, clean water is vital for any animal, but the cleanliness of the water is particularly important for mules who are very fussy about their water. Obviously a clean, safe stream has many advantages, but failing this, the water in a trough should be changed every day. In winter it is important to lag any pipes leading to troughs, put a log in the water to prevent the ice from cracking the trough, and break the ice regularly.

Additional food is generally required from September to April. Even if grass is available it is of poor quality at this time of year. Good quality hay should be fed *ad lib*, preferably out of a covered hay rack (in the field shelter is a good idea), or even on a hedge if necessary to keep it out of the mud which will inevitably form where the mule is feeding, and always in a sheltered position. Corn should not normally be necessary unless the mule is working very hard, but my mules get a small amount in winter, purely because they are running with ponies and donkeys which are all fed together, except for one elderly mule and one elderly donkey who receive a little extra separately. I prefer to use shredded beet pulp, well soaked and then mixed with bran, with occasional treats of pony nuts, sliced carrot, apple and such like.

Fencing needs to be very good for mules – some can never be kept in! They can jump over, crawl under or squeeze through practically anything man can devise, and if they fail at the fence there is always the gate. Whatever the form of fencing, barbed wire should be avoided if at all possible, in case the mule attempts to jump it.

Buildings are dealt with below, but it should be mentioned here that some shelter is needed for any animal, against heat as well as rain and wind. A certain amount of shelter can be gained from a high wall, a thick hedge, or a belt of trees, and a field shelter is even better. For one animal, anything big enough for him to back under will suffice, although something big enough to move around in (and be fed in during the winter) would be better. If there are several animals the shelter needs to be much bigger to avoid problems with kicking. The only time my mules ever kick is when they have been fed corn, and then they only warn the others off their heap.

Tethering is not really to be recommended, and certainly not for long periods, but there are times when it can be useful: to take advantage of a small area of grass, for example, or when it is the only way to stop a mule jumping out! (I have experience of this; they soon stop when they learn the reward for jumping out is a few days on a tether!) A chain must be used, because a rope or wire will become tangled. It should be long, preferably 25 feet or more, but light, and should have two swivels, one at each end; the neck strap (*not* a headcollar) should be soft to avoid chafing, and the stake should be solid, free of sharp projections, and long enough to be knocked very firmly into the ground. The requirements are flat ground with no obstructions, shelter (which may mean moving the mule every time the wind changes, as well as when it has eaten up the grass) and water. The mule should preferably be under observation all the time, and should be checked frequently. Care must be taken when first tethering him that he does not rear and go over backwards, although I have found mules take very well to tethering, as they do not panic when first restrained, nor get tangled up in the chain. But they are very strong and crafty, so every part of the tethering equipment needs to be extremely sturdy and checked regularly.

Grooming must not be overdone when the mule is kept out, or his natural weather protection will be removed. Only the dirt should be brushed out. In any case, mules love rolling – it is possibly their greatest pleasure in life – and they will soon undo all your work in grooming them!

Two final points. Practically every animal likes company (although mules are not always very nice to their 'friends') and if no other equines are kept, a sheep or goat will do. I even know of several firm friendships between ducks or poultry and equines. Cattle or sheep have the advantage that the mule will be less prone to worms if they share his field. Last, but not least, fencing, food, water and health should be checked at least once a day, but preferably more often.

In the stable

It is not normally necessary for a mule to be kept in a stable, particularly if he is bred out of a native pony, as most British mules are. Many mules, in fact, dislike being fastened inside, whatever the weather (even in the Alaskan winter), although having company often helps with this. However, most mules appreciate a stable in very bad weather, particularly if they have the choice of when to go into it and when not to, except perhaps at nights or in the worst blizzards. A stable is also useful if it is very hot and there are a lot of flies; if there is too much grass or it is too rich; if the acreage is very small; if the mule is ill; as a confined space in which to carry out early handling; and before showing or other events. It *is* possible to keep a mule permanently stabled, but it is not to be recommended. Very careful feeding, regular exercise and a good deal of extra work are needed, and mules, being so intelligent, soon get bored – although they do not seem to develop bad habits such as crib-biting and wind-sucking.

As for a horse, the stable should be light, roomy, high enough to prevent him from banging his head when he throws it up, a wide enough door to prevent him knocking himself when going through, well-drained, well-ventilated but not draughty, strong enough to withstand kicking (and mules can be strong kickers when they want to be), and with a mule-proof fastener on the door (and mules can open almost anything).

Wheat straw is considered by most people to be the best bedding since it remains springy longer than oat straw and barley straw contains scratchy seed-heads. Wood-chips or peat litter are good for making a thick absorbent layer, particularly if drainage is poor, or for animals which blow themselves out by eating their straw bedding, and mules can and do eat wheat straw quite happily.

A stabled animal needs daily grooming, not only for appearance's sake, but for the health of his skin. Sweat and dust which would clog the pores are cleaned out and muscles massaged. Eyes, ears and so on should be wiped clean, mane and tail combed and – particularly important in a stabled animal – feet cleaned out.

Regular exercise is essential for a stabled animal, particularly for a mule, which thrives on exercise. An hour should be left after a feed and before exercising, for the sake of his digestion, and an exercise period is started by walking him for ten minutes to warm up his muscles and avoid strains. If he gets hot, he should be walked for as long as it takes to cool him down before being taken back inside – if this is impossible, he should be led about inside until he cools down, or covered with a rug until he is cool. He should also be given the opportunity to roll on coming out of the stable, and, if he wishes, before entering it again. The army realised the importance of rolling, and orders included allowing the mule to roll every evening when his harness or pack was removed and before picketing and feeding.

Health

Mules are normally very healthy, strong of hide and foot, have a strong instinct for self-preservation, and are unlikely to cause any worries from a health viewpoint, suffering less than other equines from most diseases.

However, the mule's appearance, temperament and mannerisms should be carefully studied, so that if any changes do occur, they will be noticed when the regular inspections are made, and prompt action can be taken. Equines tend to go downhill quickly, and if there is any doubt, a veterinary surgeon should be called in at an early stage.

I have often been asked whether mules, horses and donkeys can be kept together because donkeys are said to pass on lungworm, but as long as a proper worming programme is maintained for all of the animals, this causes no problems. *Very* occasionally mules are known to suffer from lice, sweet itch and laminitis, but such cases are few.

Mules' feet are hard and seldom cause trouble through cracking, chipping or seedy toe, but they do not grow very quickly and turn up at the toe as donkeys' feet do if neglected. Depending on the particular mule, and the work he is doing, his feet should be cut back every eight to ten weeks, probably slightly less frequently than the recommendation for horses, and unless he is doing a good deal of road work he will not normally need to be shod. (A very few mules have white socks and therefore whitish hooves, and they are more likely to need shoeing.) If shod, he needs shoes to be specially made, because mules' feet are U-shaped rather than round like horses' feet. I have seen mules with horse-shoes 'cobbled' to fit them, and it is not a pretty sight!

101

Training

Advice on the training of any equine could fill several books but, as before, this section concentrates on the differences between the training of mules and that of horses and donkeys, which are based on the mule's unique personality. A mule is no more difficult to train, but it is necessary to understand the mule, to plan his training carefully, to keep one step ahead of him. Correct training is very important because a nervous but good-natured youngster can, by incorrect handling and training, be turned into a vicious, bad-tempered adult, whereas a correctly trained mule which has learned to trust you under all circumstances is a useful, helpful, friendly, affectionate animal – a joy to own.

A nice story, by Montaigne, illustrates the need to 'think mule', to understand *why* your mule is 'playing up' so that, instead of punishing him, you can take the appropriate action to remedy the situation without upsetting him. Thales, the philosopher, had a mule which, laden with salt, happened to stumble when fording a river, so the sacks she carried became wet. When she realised that the salt, because the water had 'melted' it, grew lighter, every time she came to water in the future she jumped in, together with her load. Her master, thinking this over, realised why she had suddenly taken to jumping in the water, and commanded that instead of salt she be loaded with wool, which when wet became heavier. 'The Mule, finding herself deceived, used her former policy no more.'

First handling of a young foal

Because of a mule's nature, it is important, if at all possible, that handling should start at birth. He is untrusting, but in this way will start at an early age learning to trust people; he is strong-willed, but in this way will start at an early age learning that his owner is in charge.

Young mules are very active; precocious – they will test people (and other equines) to see how much they can get away with; but untrusting and quick to defend themselves the only way they know how – by kicking.

It is easier at the beginning to work with the foal's mother present to give it courage and security, and in a confined space so that it cannot get far away. Gentle scratching in the favoured places is a good start – at the side of the tail, at the base of the mane, below and behind the ears, gradually spreading all over the body, legs and head, keeping movements slow and deliberate so as not to frighten him. As at all stages, nothing must be forced, because he will just react against it. Sessions should be short and varied, to avoid him becoming bored, and anything which might frighten him must be avoided, or stopped immediately if he becomes disturbed.

If at all possible the foal should be running with another animal with which it can make close friends, particularly if it is not still with its mother. One of the greatest training ploys is jealousy: mules are very jealous creatures, and if a mule sees his friend getting some fuss or a treat, he will not want to be left out. If the young mule tries kicking or makes a grab at the treat, simply walking away from him will upset him and bring him to his senses; he will almost certainly follow meekly behind. The friend, of course, should already be quiet and trusting and well-behaved, so that the mule foal will learn from it what is and is not allowed, and that people are trustworthy and safe to be approached.

When the army had to train unhandled mules in a very short time, they tied them up to handle them, but I always feel that the 'trust' learned this way is rather doubtful. If time is not important, I much prefer to leave the mule free, make lots of friendly overtures and moves to make it jealous, and let it come to me in its own time. In some cases, this has been at the age of a few weeks, and in one case it was nearly three years, but it came in the end, and patience paid off.

Once the mule has learned trust, it can gradually be taught to accept a halter and a headcollar, which can be put on every day and taken off every night. It is best taken off every night in case it gets caught on anything, and also the mule gets used to the extra contact with people which this entails. If a mule is not keen on accepting something new such as a halter, I play the 'only people with halters on can have pony nuts' game (or Polo mints, or some other preferred treat). This has never failed me yet. I demonstrate on a friend first, then try it on the foal, saying what I am doing as I do it: halter on, pony nuts, fuss, halter off, more fuss, halter on, pony nuts . . . In the early stages, feeding by hand is helpful, as it accustoms the young mule to hands touching his face. However, as soon as he starts to *demand* a treat, or to become pushy or nippy, the treat should be cut out and he should be rewarded with praise.

When starting to lead the foal, it is helpful to have someone known to him who will walk behind him. He must not be allowed to discover that he is stronger than a human, or learn that he can get away with any silliness. Mules learn very fast – they usually only need to be shown something once – and it is much more difficult for them to *un*-learn something incorrect. It can also be helpful to have another friend (if there are any left by now!) walking in front and leading the foal's mother or friend and giving it a treat, so he will want to keep up with her. This way he is being asked to do something he wants to do, rather than having someone else's will forced on him.

Following! (Photo: Meredith Hodges.)

This is a good time to start grooming him gently (he will like this in the favoured places) and picking up his feet, particularly the back feet, which will not be too popular, so should be started young. Scratching beside the tail keeps him occupied while this is being done, and sometimes giving him a bucket of corn can help, although some mules are so keen to keep their corn to themselves that they are more likely to kick, not less.

Talking to the mule all the while is very important, even if other people do think this a little odd. The words which will be employed later should be used, such as 'Walk', and 'Whoa', so he gets to know them, but also just to get him used to the voice and taking notice of it. Mules have very sharp hearing and can be trained to work without a bit, on voice alone, and all this helps. Remember, 'you can talk to a horse, but you can chat and whisper to a mule'.

Handling and training a mule are much like dealing with a human. Human babies are sometimes in a naughty mood and while maintaining a certain level of discipline, allowance should be made for the odd burst of high spirits. Also, sometimes the mule will mentally seize up from an overload and needs praise and reassurance. If he can learn to trust people when he is frightened or confused, this will pay dividends ever afterwards. Certain things, however, should *not* be allowed, and the mule should be taught what these are at an early stage, for example, nipping and kicking can be faintly amusing in a tiny foal, but dangerous in a big strong adult. Quite often simply saying 'No' loudly and very firmly can be enough to stop him (I have literally reduced a mule to tears merely by saying 'No' – and he never did the same thing again!); a sharp spank on the rear can work wonders, but perhaps the worst 'punishment' is to ignore him while making a fuss of the others.

However, punishment is to be avoided if possible – it creates a bad relationship. It is much better to arrange the situation for success (this can be a real challenge but is quite possible with some forethought) so he can be rewarded. Mules cannot be *forced* to do anything, because, like human children, they are most likely to react against it. They must be asked to do something which they perceive to be pleasant and safe.

Most of what has been said here is equally applicable to an older but unhandled mule, particularly the idea of handling another animal so that the one being trained will see that people can be trusted, what is/is not allowed – and that the other one is being rewarded with something tasty!

The next stage

Although a mule matures more slowly than a horse, and should therefore not be

The first harnessing lesson, drawn by Bonnie Shields.

B. Shields

doing any work before three or four years old (and heavy work should wait until he is five or six), it is highly advisable to continue handling the mule and keep up basic training – lungeing, long-reining and so on – as soon as he has learned to lead. Being so strong-minded and intelligent, he can easily get out of hand if just turned away for a year or two, although it is true to say that early training is never forgotten. This training is done as one would for a horse, but bearing in mind the principles already given.

One or two other points should also be borne in mind. If several attempts have been made to get the mule to do something and he has not understood, or chosen not to do it, the training session should be finished on success by asking him to do something simple and nice; when the next training session starts he will almost certainly do at once what he refused to do before – a matter of pride, I suspect! Many is the mule owner who, unwisely, I admit, has given up in despair after several unsuccessful attempts to get their mule to do something, thrown down the reins or lead rope, shouted, 'Oh, —, *don't* do it, then!' and stormed off; at which the mule instantly does whatever it was supposed to do – with a twinkle in its eye! Mules have a great sense of humour, and will often put people to the test, perhaps by refusing to do something which they have always done happily before.

Patience is the key to everything – as with any animal. Mules are more intelligent than most people realise, can understand an enormous amount, and *need* to have it made clear exactly what is wanted and what is not wanted. Even unbroken mules can behave beautifully, particularly if approached and handled confidently as though it is certain they will do what is required. Mules, incidentally, always seem to rise to the

Charlotte Bedinger lungeing her three-year-old hinny, Lukas.

occasion. I have taken unbroken or only partly broken mules to various events, on television, on an army parade where they were inspected by HRH The Prince of Wales, and they have without exception behaved like real professionals.

Mules will accept *anything* provided they can understand it, but enjoy 'spooking' at strange objects, so it is important to introduce them to all manner of strange things at an early stage.

Finally – remember, every man gets the mule he deserves!

6 The mule today – and tomorrow

There are approximately 15,500,000 mules in the world today (this and the other figures given here are based on figures from FAO for 1987), and the number is increasing each year. This figure represents approximately 12 per cent of the world's domesticated equine population, donkeys making up 32.5 per cent and horses the rest. Of the 15,500,000 mules probably only about 100,000 are used for leisure, the remainder earning their living.

The distribution of mules throughout the world is, of course, very uneven, being greater in warmer climates, with the exception of most of central Africa, where the donkey has never penetrated in great numbers and horses do not thrive in the tropical climate. Mules are also found in cooler countries which have not had a history of big, strong working horses (see over).

Asia has by far the most mules, with 5,770,000 which is 37.8 per cent of the world's total, and 5,113,000 of these being in China. Turkey has 210,000, India 134,000 and Iran 123,000. North and Central America have the next largest total with 3,556,000 (23 per cent of the world total), of which Mexico has 3,130,000 (at 1.6 mules to the square kilometre the highest density of mules in the world) and the Dominican Republic 101,000. South America comes next with 3,224,000 mules (21.1 per cent of the world total), Brazil having the highest number at 1,950,000, followed by Colombia with 600,000, Peru 230,000, Argentina 165,000 and Ecuador 105,000. These five countries are among the fifteen in the world with the highest number of mules.

Africa has 2,248,000 mules (14.7 per cent of the total), the highest number being in Ethiopia with 1,490,000 (1.2 mules per square kilometre, the second highest density in the world), followed by Morocco with 470,000 and Algeria 160,000. Europe comes very much last in the league table, with a mere 445,000 mules in total (2.9 per cent), the only country in the world's top fifteen being Spain with 129,000 mules. Oceania has an insignificant number.

Over the period 1979/81 to 1987, numbers in Asia had increased by 20.9 per cent and in South America by 15.2 per cent, numbers in Africa and in North and Central America stayed much the same, and only in Europe did they fall – by a massive 25 per cent!

These figures are significant as a pointer to the position of mules. As will be shown in the following pages, numbers in highly developed countries continue to fall rapidly

The approximate world distribu
book, 1987. The northern bound
numbers north of this, as they wi

S. AMERICA	AFRICA	EUROPE
Argentina	Algeria	Albania
Bolivia	Botswana	Belgium
Brazil	Cape Verde	Bulgaria
Chile	Egypt	France
Colombia	Ethiopia	Greece
Ecuador	Lesotho	Ireland
Paraguay	Morocco	Italy
Peru	Namibia	Luxembourg
Uruguay	Somalia	Portugal
Venezuela	S. Africa	Spain
	Sudan	United Kingdom
	Tunisia	Yugoslavia
	Zimbabwe	

USSR

ASIA	NORTH and CENTRAL AMERICA
Afghanistan	
Bhutan	Barbados
Burma	Belize
China	Canada
Cyprus	Costa Rica
India	Cuba
Iran	Dominican Republic
Iraq	El Salvador
Israel	Guatemala
Jordan	Haiti
Korea DPR	Honduras
Lebanon	Jamaica
Pakistan	Mexico
Saudi Arabia	Nicaragua
Syria	Panama
Turkey	Puerto Rico
	Saint Lucia
	Trinidad & Tobago
	USA

mules, based on figures in FAO, *Production year
nly approximate; mules will be found in very small
eral other countries not shaded on the map.

with increasing mechanisation, but this is far from the case in the rest of the world, where mules find an ever more important place.

Mules in developing countries

As mules spread throughout the world many centuries ago, they took their place alongside other animals as workers, including horses, donkeys, camels, llamas, oxen, yaks, water buffaloes and elephants. Much the same work is still done by large numbers of mules, particularly in South America, North and South Africa, the Middle East and Asia (with the exception of the southeast).

In most of these countries 'progress' has been patchy, and mechanisation with it, the largest cities having many motor vehicles, but also many working animals. Cairo, the largest city in Africa, is a good example, with many thousands of horses, donkeys and mules hard at work among its bustling, traffic-laden streets.

Rural areas, on the other hand, are usually almost completely unmechanised with few roads fit for motor vehicles. In any event, poor people could not afford to buy, run and maintain a motor vehicle. In the past tractors and lorries were often given as part of aid packages, but they soon broke down and repairs often proved impossible. This type of inappropriate aid has been much reduced, and the trend now seems to be for the introduction of more appropriate aid which includes giving people mules or mule-breeding stock, and teaching them how to use them. The lower illustration shows one of a group of students from developing countries taking a course at Shuttleworth Agricultural College, which included learning how to do farm work with mules – and also how to make the harness and implements. The mules belong to the University of East Anglia's School of Development Studies, and are used to assess mules' abilities and their relevance to the needs of developing countries.

Animals are in most countries part of the culture and tradition, which motor vehicles most definitely are not. The new owners do not become dependent on a foreign power for parts and fuel; they can be looked after easily by women and even

(*Opposite page*)

(*Top*) Urban work for a mule in Tunisia, 1989. (Photo: Andrew Mattick.)

(*Bottom*) Overseas student learning to work a mule with a cultivator, Shuttleworth Agricultural College, 1988. (Photo: Andrew Mattick.)

young children; everyone understands them; they increase a man's status in the community; they are multi-purpose (pack, draught, saddle and agriculture); they need no roads; they produce a useful by-product (dung for heating) and finally they can be eaten!

In some cases, either horses or donkeys are already being used, but mules are considered to be more suitable. On the Kenyan island of Lamu the donkeys were poor, and not really up to the work required of them, so the International Donkey Protection Trust has introduced a good-quality local pony stallion and encouraged the people to take their donkeys to him to breed hinnies, which will be more able to stand the work.

Mules are used to carry packs, particularly in mountainous areas where there are

Ploughing with a mule outside Amman, Jordan, 1989. (Photo: Chris Larter.)

few roads, such as the Himalayas and the Andes. Some countries such as Iran have good main roads but few and poor side roads, so large numbers of pack mules are essential. Afghanistan has over 30,000 mules, mostly used for pack work. The mountainous areas of South America use large numbers of mules because carrying goods in pack is often the only possible means of transport away from the towns. Pack loads are generally 25 per cent of bodyweight, but more can be carried if necessary for short distances and in good conditions.

It is in draught that mules are most widely used, either on the land doing all types of agricultural work (FAO estimates that animals provide 25 per cent of global energy input for agriculture), or pulling carts and wagons carrying every conceivable type of goods.

Pack mule in Aliazidiah, Jordan, 1989. (Photo: Chris Larter, by courtesy of SPANA.)

115

Draught mule near Larnaca, Cyprus, 1986. (Photo: Chris Larter, by courtesy of Brooke Hospital.)

(*Opposite page*)

(*Top*) Draught mule in Multan, Pakistan, 1985. (Photo: Vicki Jerome.)

(*Bottom*) Draught mule (well, nearly a mule; this is Dragon Foal) in China. (Photo: Dr Ann Chandley.)

If the load is dragged, a mule can pull its own bodyweight, but on a wheeled vehicle it can pull twice its own bodyweight, so obviously if the terrain allows, this is more economical than pack. Mules are also used to power water pumps, mills and other agricultural machinery.

The use of mules in China is worth a special mention, not because the uses are different, but because of the enormous number of mules bred there. The government recognised their value in improving China's agriculture some decades ago, and deliberately set out to encourage the breeding of mules in large numbers on farms specially set up for this purpose. The Chinese were pioneers in the use of artificial insemination in mule breeding to make it possible to breed large numbers more quickly. China's mule population of 5,113,000 is enormous, and although China is a big country, it comes fourth in the table of mule density at 0.5 mules per square kilometre.

The number of mules in developing countries is increasing for many reasons. Agriculture and industry are growing and improving and more power and transport, which are vital to both of these, need to be available locally in large quantities, cheap to buy and maintain (mules' fuel is easy to grow locally!) and easy to work with and care for. Mules, or in some cases hinnies, can usually be bred from whatever horses or donkeys are available locally, without the need to buy them in.

Much of what has been said applies to other animals, too, but mules have advantages over most in terms of speed, strength, stamina, health, sure-footedness and ease of management.

In the future it seems likely that the present trends will continue, of introducing mules to areas where they have not been used in the past, and of continuing to use them in other areas which have had them for centuries, as road-building and the spread of wealth seem to be generally fairly slow.

It should perhaps be mentioned that in many cases the owners of mules are poor and have difficulty feeding and caring for themselves and their families, never mind the mules. The mules, however, have to keep working, because without them the family's income would be little or nothing, and then they would all starve. This problem coupled with ignorance of correct methods of care and management, and in some cases with traditions of animal management which we consider unsuitable, such as the fairly common tradition that an animal should not be killed even to put it out of its misery, all lead to much cruelty, much of it unintentional. We must therefore praise and support organisations such as the Brooke Hospital for Animals in Cairo, the International League for the Protection of Horses, and the Society for

An outing on a hot day in Portugal, 1989. (Photo: Wendy Cowan.)

the Protection of Animals in North Africa, which do wonderful work in caring for the animals and educating their owners.

Mules in poor areas of developed countries

Many countries which we think of as highly developed do, in fact, have areas which are not yet fully mechanised. These can be categorised in most cases as remote rural areas with poor agriculture, poor roads and difficult terrain, and also climates favourable for donkey and therefore mule breeding. Several European countries have such areas, and use many mules for agriculture, logging, pack work and draught, notably the southern parts of Spain and Portugal, France, Italy, Greece, Bulgaria and Yugoslavia.

Pack mule, Èze, southern France, in 1960. (Photo: Harold Gayther.)

A strong Spanish mule offered for sale in Central Spain. The asking price in 1988 was 170,000 pesetas (approximately £950). (Photo: James Connolly.)

Holidaymakers who leave the coastal resorts and go inland will find many mules working, principally in agricultural work on small farms where a tractor is not economic, or where hillsides are too steep. In all these areas, mechanisation is encroaching, and it seems likely that the younger generation will prefer tractors to mules, so they will cease to be used except in very few cases where tractors cannot do the job.

Mules in highly developed countries

In the USA and Canada, Australia and New Zealand and Northwest Europe, the internal combustion engine has almost completely taken over, with a very few exceptions, from horse-, donkey- or mule-power. However, in these countries we are mostly concerned with mules for leisure, and leisure time is increasing in all of them.

USA

The USA was, in the nineteenth and early twentieth centuries, the world's biggest user of mules, but mechanisation was quick to spread to most areas, delayed by the depression in the 1930s. From five and a half million mules in 1920, by the mid 1950s the numbers of mules being used on farms, plantations, canals and roads was down to around one and a half million, and still falling. Despite this trend, there have remained pockets of people who, either because of their religious beliefs, such as the Amish, or purely because they like the old-fashioned ways, continue to use their mules.

There are also, of course, some mountainous areas where mechanisation is more or less impossible and mules are still used for the old tasks: riding over rough country to round up cattle, or taking equipment and materials up mountainsides in pack. An example of this a few years ago which received wide publicity was in one of California's Wilderness Areas where a dam needed repair, but helicopters could not be used to take materials to the remote area because they were banned for environmental reasons. In any case, helicopters have their limitations in bad weather and where goods need to be landed on steep hillsides, apart from being extremely expensive.

In addition, a few people are turning again to heavy horses or to mules for a variety of reasons: economy (for example, in 1988 when many American farmers were having a hard time, some used mules to hoe weeds from crops rather than pay the cost of spraying to kill them off), because mules do not compact the ground or damage crops, sentiment, nostalgia, protection of the environment (no noise or fumes), use of scarce resources (and there is always the gain of manure) or just because they like the pace of life and the joy of working with mules.

No doubt those who used mules for work in the past also used them for hunting, for visiting or other leisure activities, but the use of mules solely for leisure really began to take off in the 1960s, as people had more time and money for leisure. The American Donkey and Mule Society was founded in 1967 by Paul and Betsy Hutchins and Carl Wilson, largely because Betsy was horrified to read that mules were 'more or less extinct' and was determined that they should not be. The ADMS

122

acts as a national coordinating body for the many hundreds of local clubs which have gradually sprung up throughout the country, and continue to do so.

Probably the biggest single attraction for mule-lovers in the USA is Bishop Mule Days, held at Bishop in the Californian mountains on the last weekend in May (Memorial Day weekend) each year. Large numbers of mules were always used in and around Bishop, originally to take prospectors into the mountains, and in more recent times to take holiday-makers into the mountains for hunting or just riding and walking trips. When the Chamber of Commerce were looking for something to attract more tourists to Bishop, they came up with the idea of a mule show – and this has now grown out of all recognition.

The schedule of this 'show' for 1989 is shown in the illustration overleaf. The 110 classes, some for donkeys but mostly for mules, include special classes for young riders, English and Western riding styles, novice mules and donkeys, working hunter, hunter hack, jumping, dressage, coon jumping (a special style of jumping from a standstill with the owner standing at the mule's side, encouraged when out racoon hunting, as the mule had to jump over barbed wire fences), trail classes, cow working, musical tyres, barrel race, keyhole race, pole bending, run ride and lead, bed roll race, burro arena race (burros supplied; one person holds the burro, all burros start in centre of arena, burro ridden bareback, first rider aboard burro to reach outer fence without assistance of handler the winner!), cattle penning, steer stopping, team roping, racing, chariot racing, chuck wagon racing and mule speed shoeing.

There are a number of packing competitions: individual scramble contest (one packer, one horse, one mule, two boxes – catch your mule, load it and ride the horse leading the mule to the finishing post), box hitch contest, diamond hitch contest, packing contest (all these for the World Packing Championships); team packing contest, packing scramble (one packer, one swamper being the packer's assistant, one horse and two mules, nothing left on horse and mules other than headcollar, packer and swamper lie down under pack covers, on signal catch stock, saddle up, pack mules and lead pack animals around arena to finish line), team packing – comedy, team packing scramble, pack train (all these for the World Champion Packing Team). Finally there is the five-mule loose herd race, classes for mules of Thoroughbred type, draft type and Quarter Horse type, for model saddle mule, model pack mule, mule teams, five mule strings or group, a pulling contest and driving classes. In past years they had a (human) braying contest, and I cannot help feeling rather sorry that this seems to have been left out now. Around 1,000 mules

Mule Days Schedule

Mule Days, Bishop, California, 1989.

Thursday, May 25

8:00 a.m. – Show Office Opens
9:00 a.m. – Thursday Race Entries Drawn
1:00 p.m. – Mule Show – English, Snaffle Bit,
Bridle Reined and Racing Classes
6:30 p.m. & 9:00 p.m. – **MICHAEL MARTIN MURPHEY
CONCERT**

Friday, May 26

8:00 a.m. – Driving Classes and Dressage Class
1:00 p.m. – Prelim Events
2:00 p.m. – **AUCTION** – Mule & Horse Sale
6:00 p.m. – Mule Show – Prelim Events
9:00 p.m. – Country/Western Dance

Saturday, May 27

10:00 a.m. – Parade
9:00 a.m. – 5:00 p.m. – Art Show – Fairgrounds and City
Park
1:30 p.m. – Grand Entry and Mule Show
4:30 p.m. – Barbecue
7:30 p.m. – Mule Show and Speed Shoeing Contest
9:00 p.m. – Country/Western Dance

Sunday, May 28

7:00 a.m. – Lions Club Pancake Breakfast – City Park and
Fairgrounds
8:00 a.m. – Mule Show & Speed Shoeing Contests
9:00 a.m. – 5:00 p.m. – Art Show – City Park and
Fairgrounds
1:30 p.m. – Mule Show
4:30 p.m. – Barbecue
7:30 p.m. – Mule Show
9:00 p.m. – Exhibitor's Dance

Monday, May 29

8:00 a.m. – Pancake Breakfast – Fairgrounds Only
9:00 a.m. – 5:00 p.m. – Art Show – City Park and
Fairgrounds

**PROFESSIONAL INVITATIONAL WESTERN ART SHOW
SATURDAY, SUNDAY, MONDAY**
AT THE FAIRGROUNDS
ARTS AND CRAFTS SHOW AT THE CITY PARK
Show Schedule Subject to Change

'They give their riders a fright now and then.'

gather at Bishop for this event – a sight which many mule enthusiasts dream of seeing one day.

There are, of course, many other mule shows in the USA, numbers having risen from four in 1967 to over 300 in 1989, and Bishop is not the only place to call itself 'Mule Capital of the World', but it does seem to hold the biggest and best show.

Another use of mules which is very well known is for the trek down Bright Angel Trail which takes thousands of people every year down the Grand Canyon – with no passengers lost, despite the fact that many have never ridden before, and despite the steep, narrow, winding uneven trail with thousands of feet to drop over the edge. (Riders are told before setting out that if they stop, they should turn the mule's head to face the edge so it can see where the edge is!) Knowing mules' quirky sense of humour, I expect they give their riders a fright now and then!

Bishop Mule Days: the grand entry, 1979. (Photo: Bonnie Shields.)

Included in the Bishop Mule Days programme is racing, and mule racing, complete with parimutuel betting, is now big business. Mules only race against themselves, not against horses, and I am told that, mules being mules, they occasionally decide they have had enough and stop dead. You cannot blame them, I suppose, and it all adds to the fun for the spectators, but it must be a little frustrating for the jockeys.

Show jumping, dressage, eventing, long distance riding, and driving trials are, again, all events at which mules do well, sometimes competing against other mules, sometimes against horses. There have been occasions when mules have done so well

(*Opposite page*)
(*Top*) Bishop Mule Days: the packing scramble, 1979. (Photo: Bonnie Shields.)
(*Bottom*) Bishop Mule Days: the team roping contest, 1986. (Photo: Meredith Hodges.)

127

Jumping in the USA: Leslie Busque and Lucky Three Ciji in fine style. (Photo: Meredith Hodges.)

(*Opposite page*)

(*Top*) Gary Stapleton driving Jud and Lil on the 1985 Appalachian Wagon Train. This annual non-competitive event is run over five days, with participants wearing appropriate early-nineteenth-century costume.

(*Bottom*) Pennsylvania farmer Marshall Jones in a cross country driving competition.

The American mule Mae Bea C.T. shows that mules are versatile: packing. (Photo: Meredith Hodges.)

against horses, beating them so often, that show organisers have decided in later competitions only to allow them to compete against other mules as it was not fair to the horses! The US Dressage Federation allows mules to enter its competitions, after some campaigning by mule owners, and after further pressure the American Horse Show Association, while refusing to allow mules to compete against horses in AHSA-approved competitions, invited the ADMS to join the AHSA as a division, which gives them the opportunity for recognition of their accomplishments within their own species.

Mules are also used in the many parades which Americans enjoy, and which we British rather miss out on, and in the increasing number of wagon trains, run on the simple, old-fashioned principles of the pioneers, and many other purely non-competitive uses.

Versatile Mae Bea C.T.: riding (second from right). (Photo: Meredith Hodges.)

The 1976 Bicentennial Transcontinental Great American Horse Race was, incidentally, won by a mule called Lord Fauntleroy. He galloped into the stadium at California State Fair in Sacramento to take the $25,000 first prize, having travelled the 3,200 miles from Frankfort, New York in ninety-eight days.

The increasing interest in mules over the last twenty-odd years has led to a corresponding increase in numbers of mules, from a few thousand to over one hundred thousand according to Paul Hutchins.

Before leaving the USA mention must be made of a rather unusual role for mules, which makes use of their character, in the VisionQuest organisation. These people provide non-custodial treatment of juvenile offenders, which includes such things as survival training similar to Outward Bound courses, but also something unique: wagon trains which are manned by the young offenders and a high ratio of staff, and

Versatile Mae Bea C.T.: driving. (Photo: Meredith Hodges.)

trek across the wilder parts of the USA for periods of up to a year at a time. The youngsters are expected to do all the work – which can be very hard – and to cooperate with the staff and with each other, which many of them find difficult. Some horses are used, but also large numbers of mules, to pull the wagons and, for those who have earned the privilege, to ride. The mules start off the trek unbroken and the youngsters have to tackle animals as wild and intractable as themselves. Whereas horses can be knocked into submission, mules cannot, and the youngsters learn from them that violence does not always get them what they want. With the mules they have to be kind, patient and considerate – a valuable lesson for us all!

Canada, Australia and New Zealand

As in Britain, interest in mules for leisure purposes has increased in these countries in recent years, although on a much smaller scale – so far – than in the USA. Donkeys are generally considerably larger than the average British donkey, so they do have an advantage over us in being able to produce large, useful mules with ease. There is a small but active Canadian Donkey and Mule Society, and a number of enthusiastic mule owners ride, drive and pack their mules, mostly on an individual basis, with little opportunity, because of the size of the country, to get together with other mule owners.

There was a similar society in Australia which is now unfortunately no more, presumably again very largely because of small numbers of members in a vast country, and the relatively small number of mule owners in both Australia and New Zealand are catered for by their respective Donkey Societies.

There are many individual mule enthusiasts who are individually doing interesting things with their mules. Undoubtedly the best known mule in Australia is Juanita, owned by Patsie Sinfield, and she deserves a special mention. Bred in 1972 by Mag Herbert, she is a part-Arab mare of 14 hh. Bought at five months old by Ann Walker, one of Australia's foremost experts on mules, and broken to ride, she was bought by Patsie Sinfield, an experienced endurance rider, late in 1978. Within a few weeks they had successfully completed their first trail ride together.

By November 1987 Juanita had worked her way to the top of the tree in Australia as far as total completed distance was concerned, having successfully completed 8,317 km (approximately 5,150 miles) – at least 1,000 and maybe 2,000 km ahead of her nearest 'rivals'. Although she never took a first place, she completed well in six of the Tom Quilty 160-km endurance rides, and won the 'Best Conditioned and Best Managed' trophy three times at the five day 400-km Shahzada Memorial ride, completing it five times from six starts, each time with a high placing. She has been runner up 'Horse of the Year' several times in annual distance competitions. In 1985 she finally vetted out for the first time – lame at the end of a 60-mile (100-km) ride, and again at the first checkpoint of a Tom Quilty. In 1987 she vetted out again on the fourth day of the Shahzada, her lameness probably caused by a stone bruise. These are the only three times in her 8,317 km that she has vetted out, and Patsie

133

comments: 'Whoever it was who said to me once, "That mule isn't human; it isn't flesh and blood; it's never vetted out" should be satisfied now!'

Juanita and Patsie have not competed since November 1987 because Patsie has been busy moving and building a new house, but both have been keeping fit riding in the bush around their new home, and being popular (even honoured) visitors to the local Bythorn Hunt, and plans are afoot for a return to competition in 1990.

A different type of 'endurance' event was the 1,200-km Melbourne to Sydney driving marathon in which Aileen Pamment successfully drove her 14.2 hh mule Black Douglas in 1987. They have also recently started competing in club-level horse driving trials, and won the 'novice horse' class at their first attempt. American readers will perhaps have seen Black Douglas in Colombian coffee advertisements:

Patsie Sinfield and Juanita, the famous Australian endurance mule, at a pre-ride vet check.

Aileen Pamment driving Black Douglas, the Australian mule who also appears in television advertisements.

on a train, in a supermarket, a bedroom, a kitchen and a pantry, carrying an enormous pack (which wasn't as heavy as it looked, consisting only of cornflakes!).

There are an unknown number of other mules and hinnies throughout Australia, some being ridden and/or driven, some such as Pat Streefkerk's Elum competing successfully against horses. However, with the current lack of a society and little interest from the general public, there is little encouragement to breed mules or to do anything with them.

Northwest Europe

With the exception of the Poitou region of France, nowhere in this area are donkeys

135

Jumping in Sweden: Charlotte Bedinger and her 13 hh hinny, Lukas.

136

bred in large numbers or of a good size, largely, one imagines, because the climate is not ideal for donkey-breeding and because of the existence of a wide range of high-quality horses. The one country which is perhaps an exception to this is Ireland, where donkeys were – and still are to a much lesser extent – used by farmers and others, particularly those too poor to own a horse. Hinnies were said to be more common than mules here, presumably because the donkey owners could take their jenny donkeys to a good horse stallion and breed a hinny which would be capable of more work than its dam.

There are small numbers of mules of which we know – and of course there are undoubtedly many more unknown to us – in Sweden, Finland, Denmark, Germany, Holland and northern France. The Swiss and Italian armies use mules, so they are bound to be found in civilian life also – in Switzerland it is possible to take a holiday riding mules.

Great Britain

There are still a very few mules working in this country, most doing traditional urban work such as pulling rag-and-bone men's drays, or working on smallholdings, but as the ex-army mules died off in the 1940s, 1950s and 1960s, the numbers working declined to almost nil. Interest in mules in this country was probably at an all-time low.

In 1974 I came across the first mule I had ever seen in the flesh rather than on films or television, a newly born foal bred by accident as the result of a donkey stallion beating the pony stallion on the same hillside and serving one of the pony mares. In 1976 these animals came up for sale at the farm's dispersal sale, and the mule was destined for slaughter. My husband apparently commented that she was too young and pretty to die, and some ribbing from the onlookers led to the slaughterer taking £1 profit on her. He came home looking rather sheepish with a small, worried-looking mule in tow. I was so intrigued by her mental and physical abilities, her intelligence and sense of humour (and her cunning), that I set out to discover more about mules – and, like Betsy Hutchins in the USA before me, drew an almost complete blank. Again like Betsy (although I did not know this at the time), I wrote to various magazines asking any mule owners to contact me so that we could exchange information. Also, through the Donkey Breed Society, I contacted Robert Way, who had wartime experience of mules and was the breeder and owner of the 16.1 hh Jubilee, and Sue Green, whose family used their small mule Friday to carry

The author's Frances and Sue Day haymaking in Yorkshire, 1980.

(*Opposite page*)

(*Top*) Small mules make wonderful pets. The author with Muffin and Folly. (Photo: Derek M. Tinsley.)

(*Bottom*) The British Mule Society Patron, His Honour Judge Sir Sanderson Temple, MBE, QC, driving one of his mules, Bella, in the show ring.

holiday-makers' luggage up a steep hillside to their chalets. They were most helpful and enthusiastic, as was the Hon. Robin Borwick, founder of the Donkey Breed Society, who encouraged me to start a society for mules. Thus the British Mule Society was founded in December 1978.

At this stage we knew virtually nothing about mules, except from our own limited experience, and we had no idea of whether there were many other mules in this country, or what, if anything, they were doing. All we knew was that we wanted to learn more, and that everyone else seemed to have a very poor opinion of mules and thought we were mad! We were determined to change that.

We have never been able to find out how many mules there are in Britain, but from those we know of, the number reported to us standing in fields and going through horse sales, we believe that there must be between 3,000 and 4,000 in 1990. Many people have commented that they thought theirs was the only mule until they joined the BMS; hence the large number of mules called Muffin – 'What else can you call a mule?'

It has, however, been very gratifying to discover that in fact quite a large number of people *do* appreciate mules, especially, but not solely, men who served with them in the army and are well aware of their virtues. The interest shown by many in the society's early days (and, I must add, the help we received from Betsy Hutchins) encouraged us to press on and gradually, very gradually, over the years, we have learned more ourselves, and have begun to change mules' image as the public have become better educated about them. Membership of the BMS has risen, and people are becoming more interested in doing things with their mules now they know their potential, and this has led to a demand for bigger and better mules which is beginning to be met, thanks to the recent importation of some big jack donkeys from France and of some big mules from Ireland.

I should like to examine the uses to which people in Britain put their mules in a little more detail than I have with other countries, with some specific examples. To start at the bottom (?), mules make excellent pets. They are very easy and cheap to keep compared to horses and donkeys, are very affectionate and well behaved and enjoy a close relationship with their owner. They are fascinating to study because of their intelligence, and have a great sense of humour.

However, I do not personally advocate the keeping of any equine just as a pet, because they can become bored if they do nothing, and the novelty can wear off as the owner becomes bored with them. Mules in particular are also fitter and happier when working.

140

Because in the very recent past most mules in this country have been small, the most common use to which they have been and are put is driving. Even tiny mules out of Shetlands can do this work, and can, with a light vehicle, pull two light-weight adults or an adult and two small children. Children love these small mules, who are particularly affectionate, and many adults find them easier to deal with, too.

Mules are now competing against horses in driving competitions – and sometimes winning. A good example of this is Cally, Jon Green's 11 hh mule, who was very much unwanted when she was born. To save her from being knocked on the head (literally), a couple took her in and bottle-reared her, but when she became too big and lively for their back garden, at two years old, Jon bought her and vowed that by the time she was four he would have her entered in a driving event which was organised by the club of which he was chairman, and 'show the rest how to do it'. I thought he was being rather over-ambitious, as she was so young, but I had not counted on the wonderful relationship he and Cally quickly developed, and the skill and determination they both showed.

Jon Green driving Cally. (Photo: Celia Haddon.)

After careful and rigorous training, she was entered for the Afon Argoed Driving Event in June 1989. Out of seven entries in the 12.2 hh and under section they came first, and out of thirty-five entries overall, some of them very experienced horses and drivers at national level, they came second: not bad for the first time out in competition for a four year old. Cally did particularly well in the dressage, where absolute obedience is necessary, and in the marathon, in which she came first, moving along steadily, tackling the hazards carefully and unhurriedly and finishing as fresh as when she started.

Another mule which has been doing well in competition is Paddy, Sue Day's 14 hh

Sue Day driving Paddy.

Neil Portsmouth, a disabled driver, about to take Queenie in the marathon at the National Ride and Drive Event at Windsor.

mule, which came over from Ireland. He also does many other types of work for Sue, under saddle and pulling a canal boat.

Mules are even beginning to be used for Driving for the Disabled. Their sense of self-preservation is perhaps even more important here, where their passengers are less able to escape if anything goes wrong.

RIDING

Britain's small mules make excellent mounts for children providing, as with ponies, they are carefully trained. Jon Green's Cally, having been broken to harness was, at his five-year-old son's insistence, broken to ride, and young Richard could then go

Jubilee, Poitou donkey × Thoroughbred, ready to be shown at the annual Country Fair at Chatsworth. (Photo: Caroline Dale-Leech.)

for rides on Cally with his father aboard their cob mare Jolly. Sue Green, owner of the Clovelly donkeys, still has her mule Friday, and another, Remus, which the local children ride regularly. Tish and Derek Sims started, as many of us do, with one mule, Martha Muff, and not long after buying her, went out and bought a second to keep her company – Ginger Figs, who was already broken to harness.

The bigger mules now being bred are ridden by adults, their smooth gait making them very comfortable to ride, in addition to the advantages of sure-footedness and stamina. Jubilee, Britain's biggest mule, is ridden daily. Show jumping and endurance riding seem likely to be the most popular uses of riding mules in the immediate future.

PACKWORK

It can hardly be said that large numbers of mules are used under pack in Britain, but then few horses or donkeys are used in this way either. However, there is increasing interest, on a small scale. One couple, Nell and Turlough O'Conor, have recently

Janet Boston's hinny under pack.

bought two mules to be trained ready to carry their luggage when they set off on their long-dreamed of trek around the northern Mediterranean.

The future

In all highly developed countries leisure time, and the money to enjoy it, are expected to increase, and interest in animals and country pursuits is increasing. Mules, being easy and cheap to keep and better in many ways than horses, are likely to be chosen more and more in preference to horses. Above all, perhaps, there is growing interest in learning about something different, something about which little is still known, something which has in the past been misunderstood and unfairly despised.

The size and conformation of donkeys suitable for breeding large mules are improving. More are becoming available and other breeding techniques such as artificial insemination and embryo transfer are becoming available also.

Mules are gradually being accepted, particularly in the USA, by horse organisations, allowing them to compete against horses, or at least against each other under rules laid down for horses, which improves their status.

Public opinion towards them is changing as the public become better educated. The future looks very healthy for the mule.

The author and her mule Frances at home. (Photo: *Your Horse.*)

Bibliography

Armitage, P. L. 'Jawbone of a mule from the Roman levels, Billingsgate Buildings, City of London.' *London Archaeologist*, Winter 1979

Blenkinsop, L. J. and Rainey, J. W. *Army veterinary services in the First World War*. London, 1925

Carmichael, P. *Mountain Battery*. Devin Books, 1983

Clabby, Brig. John, OBE, MRCVS. *The history of the Royal Army Veterinary Corps 1919–61*. J. A. Allen, 1963

Dent, A. *Donkey: the story of the ass from east to west*. George Harrap, 1972

Graham, Brig. Gen. C. A. L., DSO, OBE, DL. *The history of the Indian Mountain Artillery*. Gale & Polden, 1957

Gray, A. P. *Mammalian hybrids*. Commonwealth Agricultural Bureaux, Slough, 1954; 2nd edn, revised, 1972

Hagedoorn, A. L. *Animal breeding*. Crosby Lockwood, 1939

Horses and mules and national defense. Dept of the Army, Office of the Quartermaster General (USA), 1958

Hutchins, P. and B. *The modern mule*. Hee Haw Book Service, Denton, Texas, 1978

MacFetridge, C. H. T. and Warren, J. P. *Tales of the Mountain Gunners*. William Blackwood, 1973

Masters, J. *The road past Mandalay*. Michael Joseph, 1961

The Mule. Quarterly journal of the British Mule Society, 1978–

Rickell, W. L. *The misunderstood mule*. Reproductions West, California, 1976

Riley, Harvey. *The mule*. Dick & Fitzgerald, New York, 1867

Savory, T. H. *The mule*. Meadowfield Press, 1979

Sinfield, P. *Juanita the wonder mule*. Broomtail Publications, Australia, 1985

Smith, D. J. M. *The horse on the cut*. Patrick Stephens, 1982

Tegetmeier, W. B. and Sutherland, C. L. *Horses, asses, zebras and mule breeding*. H. Cox, 1895

Tylden, Major Geoffrey. *Horses and saddlery of the British army*. J. A. Allen/Army Museums Ogilby Trust, 1965

Weight, H. O. *Twenty mule team days in Death Valley*. Calico Press, California, 1955

Younghusband, Sir Francis. *India and Tibet*. John Murray, 1910

Index